HAILSTORMS
AND
HOOP SNAKES

TED STONE

Western Producer Prairie Books
Saskatoon, Saskatchewan

Cover design by Warren Clark, GDL
Cover and interior illustrations by Warren Clark, GDL

Printed and bound in Canada by Modern Press ◄▆►1
Saskatoon, Saskatchewan

The publisher acknowledges the support received for this publication from
the Canada Council.

Western Producer Prairie Books publications are produced and manufactured
in the middle of western Canada by a unique publishing venture owned by a
group of prairie farmers who are members of Saskatchewan Wheat Pool.
From the first book in 1954, a reprint of a serial originally carried in the
weekly newspaper, *The Western Producer*, to the book before you now, the
tradition of providing enjoyable and informative reading for all Canadians is
continued.

Canadian Cataloguing in Publication Data

Stone, Ted, 1947–
    Hailstorms and hoop snakes

ISBN 0-88833-137-1
1. Tall tales - Prairie Provinces.   2. Legends -
Prairie Provinces.   I. Title.
GR113.5.P7S76 1984   398.2'09712   C84-091395-8

HAILSTORMS
AND
HOOP SNAKES

Contents

Acknowledgments   vii

Something about Storytelling   1

Sporting Dogs   5

Tom Hannah   10

Selling Grain and Raising Sheep   19

Conversations about the Weather   24

Hoop Snakes   27

Bascum's   31

Back in Manitoba   38

The Old Days   42

The Worst Year   49

Out in the Country   53

Moonshine   56

More Talk about the Weather   63

Fishing Stories   65

Charlie Maystead   74

Two More Stories   77
Mostly Hunting Stories   79
Milt Moyer   86
All Them Politicians Are   90
Gossip and More   95
Morley Can't Shoot Straight   99
Farmin'   104
That Ain't the Truth, Is It?   109
Poor Sparkies   113
City People   117
Epilogue: How to Tell a Story   121

Acknowledgments

The nuclei for these stories I've collected from across North America. More than to any one person, my debt is to all the rural raconteurs and tellers of rural stories whom I have been fortunate enough to hear. Many of these tales, perhaps the majority, I've heard from more than one storyteller. Often I've heard the same story told by storytellers who live hundreds of miles apart. Stories travel freely across regions and borders, and I've heard the same tales told in Newfoundland and North Carolina, Tennessee and Arkansas, the American midwest and the Canadian prairie.

Books of local history, published by the citizens of small towns, have also been sources for stories. I recommend them to anyone interested in finding more rural tales.

I especially thank my friends and family for the stories I've learned from them, particularly my parents, my wife, and my uncle Troy Blucker of Little Rock, Arkansas, who has spent a lifetime collecting and telling all kinds of yarns and is responsible for more of these tales than any other single person.

Something about Storytelling

The place can be anywhere—out in the barn, at the kitchen table, maybe in a small-town coffee shop. But when someone says: "Why I remember when . . ." you can be sure a story is going to follow.

Before television and movies and home video games, storytelling was one of society's major forms of entertainment. Particularly in rural areas the best storytellers were respected individuals, respected because of their talents, and because of the joy they brought their communities.

On every continent storytelling has been an integral part of almost every society's history and culture. Yet, in twentieth century North America, storytelling has been relegated by many to the children's section of libraries, the repertoire of joke tellers, or folklorists' journals. This is the age of electronic communication, and it seems that most forms of conversation beyond discussions about which television channel to watch are threatened.

The electronic media aren't the sole culprits in the demise of our conversational skills though. The rigors of modern life have made an equal contribution. I remember listening to an old man in Alberta telling about the days of his youth when the trip to town

1

from the family farm was made by horse and wagon. The journey took all day, but the family always stopped along the way to visit at the homes of neighbors. "Nowadays we make the same trip in the car in twenty-five minutes," the old man told me, "but we never have time to stop and visit anymore." And the stories that were told then—told on the wagon rides to town and with the neighbors along the way—are mostly forgotten.

Storytelling hasn't been completely wiped out though. People still linger in coffee shops and general stores and post offices telling tales. Storytelling is, after all, really just good conversation. It's relating an everyday incident or recalling something from the past. It's telling a joke or relating a tragedy.

Storytelling is entertainment and companionship. Stories might have a moral or be only for fun, but they provide the basis for most of our communication and all of our literature. Storytelling was mankind's first attempt at artistic expression using language, and each of us, aware of it or not, is a storyteller. Children tell what happened in school or over summer vacations. Adults tell about things they've done in their work or on their holidays. Older people tell about earlier accomplishments.

Seasoned raconteurs are still with us too, and most rural communities have a storyteller or two who can be relied on to spin a yarn now and again. A neighbor of mine told me once that until 1939 most of his storytelling was done on Sundays when the family took the day off, except during the harvest season, to visit relatives and "tell lies." He said that 1939 was the year he bought his first tractor, and to pay for it the family decided to work Sundays for one year. "Do you know," he told me, "we've worked every Sunday since then." My friend had lost his storytelling day, but he had made a story out of how it had happened.

In cities, too, storytelling is showing new signs of life. Storytelling associations, clubs, festivals, workshops, and even schools are springing up across the continent. Together they are bringing the art of the raconteur back to prominence. Professional storytellers are growing in numbers, and their services are being sought more than ever before.

Perhaps the renewed interest is because listening to a storyteller is a more personal experience than watching a movie or television show. Storytelling is an intimate art. It is more than just the communication of words. There is a sublime understanding that is passed from storyteller to listener that defies definition. It is not just knowledge or humor that is exchanged; it is feeling too.

My own fascination with storytelling stems from a combination of sources. First, of course, is the beauty of the story itself. Beyond that, however, is the feeling of the past, of roots, that stories leave inside me. Stories, passed from generation to generation, tie us together. They, along with music, link us more directly than anything else to our heritage, and to posterity.

Stories convey emotion: joy and sadness, often humor. They give us entertainment, a personal and more alive feeling for the past, contact with the exotic, and a sense of sharing. Both storyteller and listener share the joys of a tale told anew to each generation.

For families and cultures stories are the fundamental link that binds past generations to future ones. They communicate tradition, and they teach the lessons learned by those who came earlier. Stories make us more aware of ourselves and our place in the world because they create for each of us a fuller understanding of those who came before us and those who live around us. Just as importantly, storytelling provides the psychological relief that we all need from tragic aspects of life.

Stories—oral tales—activate the imagination in a way that reading cannot. Even a story that is read out loud won't work the same magic. It doesn't provide the right spark for the imagination. In an attempt to compensate the reader somewhat for this loss, the stories in this collection are told in a fictitious setting, hoping to bring some of the magic of the oral tale to a literary form. Jake, Pete, Sparky, and the rest are not real people, but they represent what is best in the storytelling tradition.

Neither do these tales have a unifying theme in any academic sense. They are not of one type or style, or of any one region. They're just stories I've heard and enjoyed, and sometimes re-told. Their common bond is that they are all essentially rural stories, with rural characters. They are stories that rural people have shared with each other, in some cases for generations.

It is, after all, in rural areas of the country where the storytelling tradition has remained most vibrant. In the country, storytellers are still acknowledged and appreciated, and storytelling is recognized as making a significant contribution to the enjoyment of rural life. Country people across the continent share similar lifestyles, hold essentially the same values, and to a surprising extent, tell the same stories. The ones in this book are only a few of them. They are meant for the reader to enjoy, and in the spirit of storytelling's current renaissance, re-tell.

Sporting Dogs

Most towns have a favorite storyteller or two, but the town where I grew up in the 1950s was lucky enough to have three. Two of them, Pete Hawkins and Sparky Anderson, were native to Deer River, but one, Jake Peters, came to our town from the Interlake area of Manitoba when he was a young man.

Jake maintained that the place he came from was the coldest part of Canada, so a lot of his stories were built around the weather. Maybe Jake's cold beginnings had something to do with his choosing a hot occupation. He ran a combination blacksmithing and welding shop in Deer River.

Jake's usual dress was a pair of tarnished green work pants with a matching shirt that had his name embroidered above the left pocket, and he was never without his tan, greased-stained hunting cap. People used to say that the only times Jake's mostly bald head saw sunshine were when he would wipe his forearm across the top of his bean to relieve it of sweat.

Pete Hawkins had one of the best-kept farms in the area. In fact, people said his place had more paint per square foot than any farm in the country. Pete was also the only farmer we knew who waxed and polished his tractors and machinery. When he wasn't busy working Pete liked to tell stories about farming, although he was glad enough to tell any kind of yarn just so long as it had a bit of humor in it.

Sparky Anderson had a farm too, but he made more money swapping horses—or anything else that was up for trade—than he did actually farming. Sparky was a big man, square shouldered and stocky, with an ambling pace in both movement and speech. I never saw Sparky without a chew of tobacco in his mouth, or in any form of dress that did not include a pair of bib-overalls. As often as not Sparky made fun of himself in his stories, and his smile, one that showed through in his eyes even when he frowned, seemed to be a permanent part of his face.

All three men were well known in Deer River for their tall tales, which, it seemed, they could create at a moment's notice. I remember one fall day after harvest when they sat along the counter in Bert's Cafe talking about dogs. The conversation had begun with a few stories about duck hunting, but, as often happens with storytelling, the topics under discussion changed several times. After duck hunting they talked about deer, then elk, then guns, and finally, sporting dogs.

Pete Hawkins told the first canine story. He said that his neighbor, Jim McPhillips, had a dog that was hit by a train.

"Old Jim used to have a wonderful hunting dog named Sugar," Pete said. "She was a good watchdog too, and she could fight better than any dog I've ever seen. She was half hound and half retriever, and one night when I was over to Jim's she chased after a big stray dog that had wandered into the yard.

"Sugar didn't catch up to it until they were on the C.P.R. tracks behind the house. It took Jim and I a couple of minutes to get back there, but we could see from a distance that it was a terrible fight. I reckon Sugar would have won all right, but the night train came through while they were scrapping and ran over both of them.

"Jim ran over to where Sugar was lying by the tracks and grabbed her and held her and cried like a baby. I kind of gave him some time with the dog and then said, 'Now, Jim, you've got to pull yourself together. Sugar was a good dog, but she lived a pretty long life for an animal and you've got a couple of good pups at home from her.'

"Jim looked up at me and said, 'I know all that, but Sugar died thinking that stinking stray dog killed her.' "

Pete's story was followed by a couple of other accounts of good dogs known in the area, but it was only a matter of time before somebody stretched a story a little bit. That's the way it is with tall tales. They're best told when people expect the truth. The bulk of any story should seem plausible, but with a tall tale you end it with something outrageous so as to take everybody by surprise.

Jake Peters got the tall tales going by telling about a springer spaniel he had owned once that kept his tail straight as an arrow when he pointed grouse, but let it drop between his legs when he scented a covey of quail. "And if he was pointing a pheasant," Jake added just when we were about to swallow his story, "he'd just stand there and wag it."

Pete Hawkins decided he could top Jake's story so he told about a dog he claimed was the best pointer to ever come into the country.

"That dog was the prettiest bird dog I ever saw," Pete said. "She could stand at point for an hour if you wanted her to. She'd never move a muscle; you wouldn't even see her breathe unless you watched her real close. The best thing about her, though, was that she was never wrong. Most dogs will make a mistake once in a while and point a spot where a bird has been, but not old Queen. If she came to a point there was bound to be a bird there.

"Of course, being that good a bird dog made it pretty easy for me to sell her pups. One day a fellow come up here from Oklahoma and he heard about Queen so he come to see the dog. We took a little walk with her and right away he offered to buy her. Of course, I wouldn't sell, but I did tell him I could save him a pup from her next litter.

"This fellow was going back to Oklahoma the following week, and he figured it would be pretty expensive to send an untried pup all the way down there. He asked if he couldn't at least see Queen work someplace where she wasn't acquainted with the terrain; that way, he said, he'd get a better idea if a pup would be worth all the bother and expense of having it shipped to him.

"Well, we loaded Queen into the back of the pickup and drove over to the other side of New Cambridge where this fellow had some relatives. We hunted most of the afternoon and Queen did her usual fine job. And the Oklahoman decided to buy a pup.

"On the way home, though, we went through New Cambridge and stopped at the store there for a bottle of pop. When we came out that fellow says, 'I thought your dog never points unless there's a bird.' I told him that that was true, and then I saw Queen. She had gone to point in the back of the pickup.

"I couldn't understand it. Queen was up on one front foot, her tail straight as a ramrod; and she was pointing directly at a man leaned against the wall of the general store in an old straight-back chair. I was so convinced Queen wouldn't lie to me I ran over and looked under the fellow's chair, figuring a bird had to be there.

"The fellow from Oklahoma says, 'I guess your dog isn't as good as you say she is.' I figured I'd lost a sale, but I told him to just wait a minute.

"I didn't see how Queen could be wrong, but the fellow in the chair said she had been pointing like that ever since he sat down there. I asked him if he maybe had a dead bird in his jacket, but he claimed he didn't. Then I had an idea. 'Listen,' I said. 'What's your name anyway?'

" 'Bob White,' the man answered."

Everybody laughed at Pete's story, but Sparky Anderson started in on a tale of his own before they got finished.

"Now the best dog I ever had," Sparky said, grabbing at the straps of his bib-overalls and leaning back on his stool, "wasn't any fancy purebred dog like yours, Pete, but he could point as well as any dog I ever saw. He was half Airedale and half labrador retriever, and he seemed like he could do anything any other dog could do, and when he was done, he could lick the other dog.

"I found Curly—that's what I called him, Curly—runnin' along the road in front of my house. I knew ever' dog that belonged in the neighborhood so I was goin' to run him off at first, but then I got to lookin' at him and somethin' told me to just keep him. I thought he might turn out to be a pretty good watch-dog—and he did.

"I owned Curly for six months before I ever took him huntin'. Even then I didn't really expect much from him since he'd never had any trainin' that I knew about.

"The way I come to take him huntin' at all was that one fall I was watchin' one of them outdoor programs on the television. They was filmin' a bunch of ducks. Well, anyway, when them ducks quacked old Curly set right up and looked at the ceilin' tryin' to find those birds. The next mornin' I took him duck huntin'. And do you know, he turned out to be an excellent retriever. Why, he'd hit the water before a duck would, and have the bird back to me in nothin' flat. He had a real gentle mouth too.

"I took that dog duck huntin' ever' time after that, and then started takin' him bird huntin' too. He turned out to be just as good a pointer as he was a retriever. And did he ever enjoy himself on a hunt. I never saw a dog have so much fun. I swear he liked to go more than I did.

"Later on in the fall I took him bear huntin' and he acted like an old pro at it. And over the winter we shot rabbits together, with that curly-haired black dog chasin' them bunnies just like he was a beagle.

"Finally spring came and I put up my guns for the fishin' season. I thought that since the dog had turned out to be such a good hunter he'd probably like to come along on a fishin' trip too, so the first time I went to the lake I loaded my tackle in the truck and called for him to get in.

"Well, you know that dog started to get in all right, but then he backed away like somethin' was wrong. First he'd come up to me, but then he'd run back toward the house and kind of whimper; then he'd come back to the truck, then run back towards the house like he wanted me to follow him. Then all at once he took off towards the house at full throttle.

"I went after him, but he could run a lot faster than I do. My wife was sittin' on the front porch and she told me the dog ran past her with an old Campbell's soup can in his mouth. She said he was headed for the back of the house.

"Well, I went on back there, and do you know, here was that dog in the garden diggin' angle worms."

Tom
Hannah

Bert's Cafe was the local coffee stop in Deer River for anyone with a little time to waste. Partitioned from Woody Blackburn's barber shop with spruce boards and wallpaper, it was long and narrow with at least one calendar advertising lumber or farm machinery or seed grains on each wall. An oak serving counter ran from front to back, and five formica-topped kitchen tables were between it and the five restaurant booths that lined the opposite wall.

On three widely spaced shelves behind the counter Bert kept an assortment of sale goods. Bert never paid much attention to the nuances of marketing strategy, but he knew what sold in a small town. His shelves were randomly stocked with, among other things, shotgun shells, stove bolts, cigarette lighters, can openers, jackknives, candy bars, potato chips, bottles of gasoline de-icer, flashlights, .22 caliber ammunition, cigars, chewing tobacco, headache pills, rabbit's foot key chains, road maps, and automobile deoderizers shaped like pine trees. In the room behind the restaurant Bert had a card room which caused some concern for Deer River's more ardent church-goers. It was furnished with a pool table, a half dozen card tables, and an equal number of spittoons.

Bert himself was a short man with a wide girth and not more than two dozen strands of hair on his entire head. There were people in town who called him Curly, and a few who called him Shorty, and one or two who called him Tubs, but most people figured he had too many easy nicknames and just called him Bert.

One spring day Bert was a little surprised to see Pete Hawkins come in the door at noon. Pete usually worked too hard to come into Bert's every day the way Sparky Anderson did. When he did come in it was usually the first thing in the morning before the feed store opened, or late in the afternoon when most of his day's work was done and an errand of some kind brought him to town.

"Hey, you're early," Bert called as Pete came through the door. "Did you hear about the farmer who was asked what he'd do if he won the million dollar lottery?"

"I'll bet he said that he'd spend some on whiskey, women, and horseracing," said Pete. "Then he'd just waste anything that was left over, right?"

"Naw," said Bert. "He told everybody that he'd just keep on farming until the money ran out."

"That's a good story," Pete said. "But something happened to me this morning that makes a better one. I just had to come to town and tell somebody."

Just then Jake Peters came through the front door. "Looks like we're going to tell some lies this afternoon," said Bert, hitching up his pants. Sparky Anderson was already there.

"I started seeding that forty acres across from Tom Hannah's this morning," Pete began. "Old Tom was in his yard when I came into the field. I saw him there, but I didn't pay any attention to what he was doing. You know what a mess that yard of his is in.

"When I came into the field my seed drill was out of the ground, of course, and I left it up, driving diagonally across the field to the northwest corner where I drove a stake into the ground. Then I got back on the tractor and took another stake down to my southwest corner. I like to make sure my rows are straight so I'm always really careful to get the first one in a straight line.

"When I got the second stake in I was ready to go, but here come old Tom Hannah. 'What you doin' there?' he says. See, Tom saw me driving around the field with my seeder out of the ground. So I told him I was just putting in a couple of stakes so I could get my rows straight.

"Well, old Tom goes to laughing at me right out loud. 'I never bother with any of that,' he says. 'My daddy always told me you could get more seed in a crooked row.'

"The worst of it was," Pete said after a pause for everyone to laugh, "I had to stop and figure out what it was that was wrong with that kind of thinking."

"Tom Hannah is quite a fellow, isn't he?" Bert said. "He was in here last week telling me how he'd tried to fix that John Deere tractor of his with the wrong part. 'I tried to save myself a hundred dollars,' he told me, 'and it ended up costing me twice what it would have if I'd done it right to begin with.'

"I tried to make him feel better," Bert said, "so I told him, 'Well, you live and learn.' Old Tom looked at me and said, 'Yea, and then you die and forget.' "

Sparky Anderson spoke next.

"About the funniest story I ever heard about old Tom," Sparky said, "he told on himself. When he first bought that John Deere tractor of his he had a hard time gettin' used to goin' into the barn with it. The seat sets about six inches higher than his old Massey, and he had to duck his head goin' into the barn or else he'd crack it just above the brim of his cap.

"Tom was milkin' cows back then, and he said the first month he had that tractor he took it into the barn every mornin' to get the manure wagon and he hit his head every time. He said it didn't bother him too much hittin' it on the way in, but what really made him mad was that he'd hit it on the way out too.

"Anyway, he told me that he woke up one mornin' bound and determined he wasn't going to hit his head anymore. He said he thought about that doorway all the time he was eatin' breakfast; and he thought about it drivin' the tractor to the barn. He even took his cap off so he could see better, and when he got to the barn he ducked his head just as the tractor went through the doorway.

"Tom said he was so proud of himself he felt like cheerin', but he sat back up on the tractor seat just in time to bang the top of his head against the milkin' pipe. . . ."

Jake Peters had a story about Tom Hannah too.

"You remember that rocky quarter of land Tom had up the other side of Pierson's place," he said. "Tom doesn't own that quarter any more of course. Nobody from around here does. Tom told me he tried to farm that land for almost ten years, but the only thing he got for his trouble was a bunch of busted up machinery. Tom said he finally decided the only way he could ever make any money from that quarter would be to sell it at an inflated price to somebody from the city.

"Well, Tom put some ads in some big city newspaper and before too long he had a fellow come out here to look at his property. It wasn't a bad looking piece of land if it weren't for all the rocks, and Tom said it was late in the fall when the fellow came, so he was hoping it would snow and cover them up. The weather didn't cooperate though and it turned warm. Tom had to take that fellow out there to see it as it was.

"Evidently the guy took a liking to that land right off. Seemed he was just about to buy it when all at once he got to looking at all the rocks. Tom figured the best defense is an offense, and told the city fellow not to worry about the stones. He said rocks cooled the ground and helped keep in the moisture. He said most farmers wanted a few stones on their ground. 'Just kick over one of them smaller ones and take a look,' Tom told the city fellow.

"Well, that guy kicked over a stone or two just the way Tom told him to and was surprised to see it was just as he had been told. The ground was cooler underneath, and just a little bit damp. 'Well, I'll be darn,' the city fellow said. 'I didn't know about that.'

"That city fellow was just about to buy Tom's land when all of a sudden he saw the rocks Tom had piled along the fence rows. There were enough of them to build a couple of houses. 'Now just a minute,' the city fellow said. 'If them rocks is so good for the soil why do you have them piled along the edge of the field?'

"Well, Tom didn't lose a breath. 'Oh, I just had those hauled in,' he said. 'I haven't had time to spread 'em around yet.'

"I guess that fellow bought the land too, because old Tom don't own it any more."

Jim McKenzie, who had been sitting at the end of the counter eating a hamburger while the stories were being told, was the only one in the cafe who didn't laugh at Jake's tale.

He seemed to think about it for a little while. Then he said, "Do you know, I believe that story about Tom Hannah. When I was about twelve years old I wanted to get a horse real bad, but of course I didn't have much money. It seemed like any horse I could find that I wanted I couldn't afford, and any horse I could find that I could afford I didn't want.

"Anyway, Tom had this pony out there and I found out he was only asking a hundred bucks for him. I went out to look at him and the horse seemed pretty good to me. It was an Appaloosa-colored gelding with a whole bunch of little spots across both sides of his rump and a long brown and white mane that was combed out real nice.

"So to make a long story short, I bought him, took him home, and then rode him the rest of the afternoon. That evening I put him in the barn for the night.

"And what do you think? The next morning when I went to get him I found that he had died during the night. Well, I was so mad I went right in and called old Hannah.

" 'Listen,' I yelled, 'you know that horse you sold me? He died last night.'

"Old Hannah didn't say anything for a second or two, and then he spoke in a real nice voice: 'Gee, that's funny,' he said. 'He never did that when I owned him.' "

Sparky Anderson laughed longest and hardest at Jim's story about Tom Hannah. When he finally stopped he said, "Yea, old Tom is quite a horse trader. Do you know one time I had an old mare that I didn't think was worth much of anything, so I traded her to Tom for a good-lookin' little colt. I thought I'd made a pretty good trade, but before long I heard that old Tom had sold my mare for $600. I didn't think there was any way Tom's colt was worth that kind of money, so I figured Tom got the better of me. About two weeks later, though, Tom came around to the house, and although he didn't say so, I could see that he was wantin' to trade for his colt back.

"We bargained around for a while and I ended up tradin' the colt for an old gelding pony, a young mare, and a Case jackknife.

This time I figured I got the best of Tom for sure because I was able to sell the pony for $200 and trade the mare for an old Oliver tractor that was worth at least $500. That made $100 and a pocket knife more than Tom got out of my original mare.

"Anyway, things went along fine for a few months until I happened to be over at Tom's and I see the colt again. Well, by this time the little fellow had filled out quite a bit and had become quite a good-lookin' horse. Course, I tried not to let on to Tom, but I really wanted to get that colt back. Finally Tom got around to talkin' horses and the first thing you know we're talkin' trade; him tellin' me how much I need that colt and me tellin' Tom that I never want to bring another horse onto my farm.

"After about half an hour of hagglin' we drove over to my place and, before long, settle on a swap. I got the colt back and Tom got a team of ponies I'd traded for a couple of days before over in Sparta. They were a nice-lookin' team, but I found out when I got them home that one of them was balky, so I felt a little bad tradin' them to Tom, even though I knew he wouldn't hesitate none about unloadin' 'em on me. I tried to get him to throw in a model number 97 Winchester shotgun for boot, but he wouldn't go for it.

"Anyway, what do you think happens? Two days later I find out Tom has sold those ponies of mine with a little cart to somebody over New Cambridge way for $900. I mean talk about a profit! I figured old Tom had got the best of me again.

"Then a couple of months later we got to tradin' again. Tom had picked up a big gray mare somewhere, and I knew of a fellow who had another one just like her. I figured I could either sell her to him so he could have a matched team, or trade him something and get his horse. Anyway, it ended up I traded a chestnut mare and the colt, who by this time was a full-grown horse, to Tom for this gray mare. The next day I sold the mare to the fellow from Sparta for $1,200 cash money. Everything worked out just the way I had hoped it would. It didn't even make me feel bad when I heard a couple of days later that Tom had made a little money off my chestnut mare.

"It was six months before I ever saw that colt again. By that time he was a top-lookin' stallion. Tom was callin' him Champ and I traded two mares and Tom's pocket knife to get him back.

Tom made good money out of both those mares, and I sold Champ to a guy from out east who came through town buyin' horses. I got $1,700 for him.

"Then a couple of weeks later I ran into old Tom, and he asked me how Champ was doin'. I think he was wantin' to trade again. When I told him I'd sold Champ, Tom got mad as a hornet at me. 'You damn fool,' he yelled. 'Now what are we goin' to do? We've been makin' a livin' off that horse for two years.'"

Pete Hawkins told a story he had heard from Tom.

"Seems Tom bought a horse from some guy over the other side of New Cambridge," Pete said. "Tom told me the guy he bought it from was real apologetic about wanting to sell the horse. He kept saying he knew the horse didn't look so good, but he wanted to sell it anyway.

"Tom said he bought the animal cheap, but he had it home before he realized that it was blind. Tom said he didn't feel swindled though. 'After all,' he said, 'the man told me the horse didn't look so good.'"

Sparky Anderson told one more story about Tom Hannah. It was one that everyone already knew, but nobody minded listening to it again.

"I think Tom Hannah's most famous horse trade was one he made with Oscar Hoppingarner about thirty years ago," Sparky said. "Oscar and Tom and a bunch of other swindlers were in the beer parlor talkin' about horse tradin' when Tom come up with the idea of tradin' horses sight unseen.

"Well, nobody wanted to make no blind trade with Tom 'cause at this particular time he had a sorry-lookin' old horse out at his place, an old sway-backed black mare with bad legs and sore feet, and everybody knew that Tom was just wantin' to find some way to trade and get rid of her. All of a sudden, though, Oscar Hoppingarner says that he'll take Tom up on his offer. They agreed to meet the next day at noon down at the elevator and exchange horses.

"Well, the next day half of Deer River was at the elevator when Tom and Oscar arrived. Tom had a regular horse wagon, but when he opened the back gate he brought out an old sawhorse. Everybody thought it was kind of a dirty trick,

especially when they'd all been expectin' to see that brokedown nag of his.

"Oscar, he looked at the sawhorse, and then opened the back of his truck. We could all hear the animal movin' around in there so we knew it was a real live horse. Oscar pulled himself up on the truck gate, opened the back, and grabbed the bridle of the most pathetic-lookin' animal you ever saw in your life. It was about six different colors, knobby kneed, sway-backed, and just plain ugly.

"Tom Hannah just stood there with his mouth open for a minute, and then says, 'Well, I'll be damn. This is the first time I ever got beat in a horse trade.' "

Selling Grain and Raising Sheep

Deer River had a small auction barn where livestock sales were held every other Saturday during the warm months of the year. The barn was on the opposite side of the railroad tracks from town, right next to the Co-op elevator. There was a little coffee shop between the elevator and the barn that only opened on days when there was an auction.

Sparky Anderson was in front of the coffee shop one auction day leaning against the corner of the building waiting, as usual, for the sale to start, when Pete Hawkins drove up to the elevator with a load of grain to sell. Sparky watched as Pete's truck was unloaded and Pete finished his business at the elevator.

When Pete parked his truck and started towards the auction barn, Sparky called to him: "No hurry to get in there," he said. "The auction will be late startin' again. We might as well have a cup of coffee and a piece of pie."

Pete was agreeable. When they sat down at the counter Pete was talking about the grain he'd just sold. He said the price a man got for wheat hardly made it worth growing.

Sparky smiled, and when Pete stopped talking he said, "Do you know, my dad used to tell a story about a neighbor he had back before we moved up here, back when he was just a young man. This neighbor lived a couple of miles farther out from town than our family did, and he had an old jack donkey. When the neighbor took his grain to sell in town he'd hitch that donkey to the wagon and drive it to the elevator.

"Comin' home the donkey could find his own way, so as often as not on the way back from town the neighbor would be lyin' down sleepin' in the back of the wagon—and if he wasn't sleepin' he'd be lyin' there complainin' to himself about the poor price he got for his crop. But the donkey always took him home without bein' told what direction to go.

"After a few trips to town the donkey got smart enough to know where they were goin' whenever he was hitched to a grain wagon. Then the neighbor didn't have to drive either way. He'd take a nap goin' to town, and would usually be up complainin' on the way back.

"Dad said he did this for a couple of years. Then one summer Dad started seeing the donkey go by pullin' the wagon with nobody in it, so the next time he saw the neighbor he asked him about it.

"'Well, you know,' said the neighbor, 'the donkey knows the way, and I figure only a jackass should sell wheat at those prices.' "

Pete and Sparky finished their coffee and walked over to the auction barn. To look at them a stranger would have picked Pete, tall and slender and dressed in his customary crease-pressed Levi's and freshly shined cowboy boots, as the buyer, but Pete had only come that day to see what was being sold. It was Sparky, wearing bib-overalls and work boots, who headed for a seat near the ring intending to do business.

Sparky always carried cash, the bills neatly folded in his buttoned front pocket, and he bought anything at an auction from horses to goats if he saw the possibility of making a profit on the transaction. Sometimes Sparky would buy animals at one auction and sell them at another before the week was out, almost always at a good profit.

Feeder pigs were Sparky's specialty. At auction, pigs sold best in bunches of fifteen or more, but Sparky only bought them in small groups, even singles—at a discount of course. When he had enough pigs of the same size and breed to make a good-looking lot he'd sell them together—usually at top price—and almost always at an auction in a town other than the one where he first bought them.

The auctioneer was selling a dozen feeder lambs when Pete and Sparky came in. The lambs came into the ring through a gate to the auctioneer's right, and after they were sold, departed via a gate to his left. The lambs were followed into the ring by a half dozen culled ewes.

Sparky looked at the animals and said, "We used to raise sheep. Had about a hundred head, but they took too much fencin'. I liked the lambs though. I liked seein' them run in bunches across a pasture, or climbin' up and down the manure piles. It helped make all the late-night lambin' worth-while.

"Sometimes, usually when the ewe had some birthin' trouble, or the lamb was just small, we'd get little ones that were too weak to even suck. I heard someplace that a bit of whiskey given with an eye dropper would kind of fire the little fellows up, so I bought a bottle to keep in the barn. . . ."

Sparky paused and spit tobacco juice out into the ring. "Whiskey never did the lambs a bit of good, though," he said. "But I found that it helped me. a good number of times."

Pete said that his dad had raised sheep.

"What I remember most about our sheep," he told Sparky, "is my youngest sister, Janis, taking care of the orphan lambs. Janis loved all animals so as soon as she was big enough Dad turned over the chore of bottle feeding the orphans to her.

"Well, you know how tame little lambs will get when you feed them bottled milk. They'd follow Janis everywhere, just like the dogs did. We had two border collies that followed her single file any place she went, clear into town if she'd walk that far; and when she was bottle feeding them, the lambs would follow too.

"Usually, we only had one or maybe two bottle lambs. Some years there wouldn't be any, but I remember one year there were about five. Was it ever comical to see Janis then. She'd be in the lead with those two dogs next in line and the five lambs, one behind the other, following her across a field or down the road to the neighbors. It looked like a mother hen with her brood. They'd even follow her to the outhouse, and then wait outside until she came out again."

That story reminded Sparky of a tale about an orphan lamb from his farm.

"One spring we lost a ewe during a bad lambin'," he said. "But we saved the lamb all right." Dad tried to get one of the other sheep to adopt the orphan, but none of them would do it. All of our ewes were either carryin' twins or their own lambs were too big to pair up with this little new-born.

"Well, as it turned out, we had these neighbors, the Arnsteds —they lived where the Kellwoods do now, but they weren't any relation to the Arnsteds who live around here now. Anyway, they had an old Labrador dog that had pups the same mornin' our lamb was born. The dog only had three pups so we figured there was room enough for another if we could get the bitch to accept a new one.

"Now it might seem like a backwards idea to try to get a dog to raise a lamb, but it worked. The way we did it was to take the pups away. We put 'em in a cardboard box with the lamb and set the box up on the bread warmer above the kitchen stove where the mother couldn't get at 'em.

"Well, the old dog went to whimperin' and tryin' to get at the box, but we just left it sit up there for ten or fifteen minutes. Finally, the dog got to makin' such a fuss to get her puppies back that we took the box down, and she jumped in and started motherin' all four of 'em.

"We figured dog milk must be pretty much like sheep milk because that lamb grew real well, just like he had his own mother; only of course he grew up with those puppies instead of other sheep, and he began to act pretty much like a dog. He'd even eat puppy chow when it was dished out for him.

"And do you know it was a funny thing. As those pups got older, old man Arnsted left that lamb run with 'em. He called him Whitey and took him along when he took the other dogs out for their huntin' lessons. And I'll be darn if that lamb didn't take to huntin' just as if he were bred for it. Whitey wasn't all that good at retrievin' ducks; he never got the hang of swimmin', but he did fine on shore. He was an excellent bird dog and he seemed to have a good nose for rabbits.

"I remember many a day goin' over and seein' old Whitey chasin' rabbits at the front of that pack of dogs. The other dogs learned pretty quick that Whitey could keep a closer trail than they could, so they'd fall in behind.

"Anyway, it was about this time that I went into the hospital for that operation I had on my knee when I was a kid. I was gone three weeks and then when I did get home I was laid up for about a month and didn't go anywhere.

"Finally, one day, I took a walk over to Arnsted's for a visit. It's three and a half miles over there from the old farm, so I had to take it pretty easy goin'; when I got there I just sat on the back step visitin' the Arnsted boys until old Mr. Arnsted came around to see how I was doin'.

"Well, it was about that time I noticed that I hadn't seen anything of ol' Whitey, so I asked where he was.

"Mr. Arnsted got kind of sorry lookin' and said, 'Well, Sparky, I'm afraid we had to shoot him.'

" 'Shoot him?' I said. 'Why, Mr. Arnsted, you know that that lamb was turnin' into one of the finest bird dogs in these parts. Why on earth would you ever want to shoot him?'

" 'I had to,' old man Arnsted said. 'He got to killin' sheep.' "

Conversations
about
the Weather

It was a hot, very humid summer day. Pete, Jake, and Sparky sat on benches along the front of Trompkin's Store and talked about the sky. Thick black clouds gathered south and west of the town.

"Think it'll rain?" Sparky asked.

"Always has," said Pete.

"It'll miss a good chance if it doesn't," said Jake.

Both answers were standard replies in Deer River.

"I remember the summer of '31 was hot like this," Sparky said. "Even hotter through July and most of August."

"I remember that summer," Pete said. "It was so hot the cows gave pasteurized milk."

"That's right," said Jake. "We had to feed cracked ice to the chickens to keep them from laying hard boiled eggs."

"Course, it was a lot drier that summer than it is this year," Sparky said. "There were full-grown frogs that never learned to swim, and the dust was wicked. One time there was so much of it in the air I saw a gopher dig a hole six feet off the ground."

Pete said there was so much dust that blew across the prairie that summer that sometimes the soil would pile in drifts just like snow in the wintertime.

"It'd take a real pile of dirt to drift the way we had snow drifts back in Manitoba," Jake said. "I remember one winter when the snow was so deep it was piled higher than a man could reach along both sides of the path to the outhouse. We had to shovel a spot in the barnyard for the cows to stand. Then in early March we had a blizzard that completely covered the barn. Dad had to cut a hole in the roof to get in to milk the cows."

The wind picked up just a little. A paper sack blew past the men on the sidewalk. Old man Hoppingarner came out of Trompkin's Store and sat on the bench next to Jake. "You boys are going to get wet if you sit here too long," he said.

"Why, Oscar, do you think it'll rain?" Sparky asked.

"It'll miss a good chance if it don't," old man Hoppingarner said.

None of the men made a move to go into the store. "The look of that sky reminds me of the worst hailstorm of my life," Hoppingarner said. . . .

"It was on the first of August, 1918. I had a forty-bushel wheat crop almost ready to harvest, and the price was way up.

"See, I pretty well built that farm of mine from scratch. We had five kids and a house that wasn't big enough for two, and an old log barn, and . . . well, with the war on and prices good, I fell for a line some fellow was pitching for farm loans. It wasn't just me; lots of people right around here made the same mistake. I borrowed twenty-five hundred dollars, built a house and barn, and planted more seed than I'd ever planted before.

"I wasn't even home when the storm came. I was right here in town. My oldest boy played ball and there was a tournament on. After the game we came here for groceries, coffee and sugar, that sort of thing.

"The weather looked like rain. Sort of the way that sky looks right now, but there was no real warning for how bad it was going to be. I was standing in the front of the store talking with Gus Trompkin. It was a couple of months before old Gus died. All at once he looked out the window and said, 'Oscar, this is going to be some storm.' I turned and looked where old Gus was staring. The sky had turned as dark as night.

"Then it started raining, not hard, just a real light easy rain, and it was still dark and there was no wind. But the air felt different. Then it started raining harder, and just as soon as the rain came the wind picked up too, and then the hail. The street turned white with hailstones, some as big as oranges, but mostly they were smaller, more like plums. The Trompkins all lived upstairs above the store at that time, and they brought down pillows and we held them against the windows. Only one window broke. It was upstairs where nobody had been standing with a pillow.

"Then all of a sudden the hail stopped. The wind died down, and it stopped raining. The sky went back to looking just about the way it does now. The whole thing happened in about fifteen minutes.

"When we got home all the windows on the front of the new house were broken. So were the ones on the front of the barn. The first thing I did was go see the wheat. It's a hard thing to look at a good crop ruined like that. I had figured on getting forty bushels to the acre, but after that storm, I didn't know if I'd get seed enough for the next year.

"That was some summer, I tell you. Every penny we could get our hands on went to pay the interest on that loan. The next year we had a good crop, but of course the war had ended and the price of wheat dropped."

The clouds were high in the sky. Pete Hawkins said, "Well, I guess that's farmin', Oscar." Scattered drops of water began to fall from the sky. The men got up.

"Yea, that's farmin' all right," old man Hoppingarner said, "and I spent the rest of my life payin' for that hailstorm."

The men looked up at the sky, and then went back into the store.

Hoop
Snakes

People always said there were rattlesnakes in the sandhills a few miles south of town, but I don't remember how Jake, Pete, and Sparky got on the topic that day in Bert's. None of them had ever seen a rattler out there. After they discussed all the rattlesnake lore they knew, Jake Peters started telling how rattlesnakes weren't very poisonous anyway. He said that the most poisonous snakes on the continent were in Manitoba.

Well, everyone knew better than that. But nobody said a word because we knew a story was coming. That was the way it was with Jake. He'd try not to let on, but there was something about the sound of his voice that was different when he was telling a story. There was just a hint of a grin on his face when he started talking about hoop snakes.

"Now a hoop snake is about the most poisonous snake there is," Jake began. "They'll roll themselves into a hoop and bound along the countryside like a loose bicycle tire. That's why people call them hoop snakes. And if they bite somebody, the poison will kill them in three or four minutes.

"I remember one time finding two hoop snakes fighting along the edge of the river that ran past the farm where I grew up. It was a wicked fight too. Both of them snakes were flailing around in the grass, and sometimes they even tumbled down the bank into the water. All at once, though, the bigger snake got the smaller one by the tail and started to swallow it.

"Not to be outdone, the smaller snake flopped around and got the big one by its tail and started swallowing too. Within five minutes they'd swallowed so much of each other there was nothing left but about three inches of the bigger snake curled up like a doughnut."

Pete Hawkins didn't even let people finish laughing before he tried to top Jake's story.

"Now dog-gone it, Jake," he said. "Don't you know we've got hoop snakes around here too? I shot one just the other morning that was trying to nurse from a freshened cow of mine. Hoop snakes will do that, you know. The closest call I ever had with a hoop snake was once when I was a young man and saw one stealing milk that way.

"I was out in our south pasture and the hooper was nursing from an old Jersey we had then. Well, I hauled off and threw a rock at the snake. It was a fool thing to do. I know that now, but at that time I was little more than a kid and didn't know any better.

"Anyway, that snake rolled himself into a hoop and started chasing me. It didn't run me far, though, because I figured out pretty quick that it's impossible to outrun a hoop snake. I decided to stand my ground and fight him with an old walking cane I had along with me, rather than get caught from behind by that snake. I whirled around, and at the exact moment he struck at me with them poisonous fangs of his, I knocked him silly with my walking stick. The hooper, momentarily dazed, slithered away like a snake ought to crawl.

"Well sir, when I looked at that walking stick I realized what a close call I had had. There were two holes in the stick where the snake had bitten it, and the poison very quickly caused the wood to start swelling. . . . And do you know that before I could get back to the house my walking stick had swelled to the size of a fence post. . . . And by the time I got everybody out of the house to see it, the darned thing had grown to the size of a poplar tree; and by the time I got it to the sawmill, there was enough lumber in it to build an eight-by-ten-foot chicken house."

Well, everybody laughed at that, but Pete started talking again.

"Sure was too bad about the chicken house though. Pride can be a terrible thing and because I had just too much of it I plum lost my senses. See, I like to keep my buildings painted up nice and one day, without thinking through what I was doing, I painted that chicken house red. It sure looked pretty, but, of course, the turpentine in the paint started drawing the poison out, and the first thing you know that clucker coop shrunk to the size of a bluebird house." Pete paused for just a moment and then said, "We all felt lucky there weren't any chickens in it at the time."

Sparky Anderson sat quietly at the counter as the laughter died down following Pete's tale. Everyone in the cafe knew that it was his turn. He called to Bert for more coffee and a butter tart, then scratched the grey stubble on his chin. When he spoke next his voice wasn't directed towards any one person in the room, but rather to everyone at once.

"Yea," he said. "I've seen a few hoop snakes, but they never bother me much. For one thing there aren't so many of 'em as there used to be. See, all these chemicals and air pollutants and insecticides and what-not have thrown 'em out of whack and they don't breed as prolifically as they used to do in the old days. The reason for that is that nowadays all the female hoop snakes roll clockwise and the male ones are only rolling counterclockwise.

"Another reason I don't worry none about hoop snakes is that I know their weakness. I discovered it once on a fishin' trip up on Lake Manitaugosis. I'd been fishin' for pike all day, but hadn't caught a thing. I didn't mind much comin' up empty handed though 'cause I was just enjoyin' the fresh air, and besides that, I'd brought a bottle of Seagrams along with me as snake-bite remedy just in case I ran into any hoop snakes. I kept it in my back pocket and ever' once in a while I'd test it to make sure it wasn't spoiled.

"About the time the sun was getting ready to go down, though, I remembered a tree frog I'd caught that mornin' and I decided to try it for bait. I figured it might get me one of those big northerns that hang around the shallow waters of the lake. Well, I put that frog on my hook, bein' real careful not to hurt him too much, and cast my line up towards shore. I cast a little too far though, because that tree frog almost ended up on dry land. And when I started to reel my line in I figured I must have snagged some weeds or something from the beach because the line dragged so funny.

"When I got it all reeled in, though, I found out what the trouble was. There was a hoop snake had hold of my frog, and I'd pulled him into the boat with me. He didn't do anything, just hung there at the end of my line with a tight hold on my tree frog.

"Now I'll tell you the truth. I didn't know what to do. Then I remembered that Seagrams that I had in my back pocket, so I reached around and grabbed the bottle—being real careful to keep a good hold on my fishin' pole. I opened the Seagrams with my teeth, and poured about a shot and a half of that firewater into the hooper's mouth. . . . And I want to tell you, that snake let go of that frog and went to floppin' around in the boat like he'd been poisoned. Then he shot out of there like somethin' was after him, and swum off towards shore.

"After I caught my breath I went back to fishin'—but I didn't use no more tree frogs for bait. No sir, I'd seen all the hoop snakes I cared to see for one day. Then something funny happened. I hadn't had time for more than about two casts when I felt somethin' rubbin' up against my ankle. I looked down and here was that hoop snake with two more tree frogs in his mouth."

Bascum's

Trompkin's was the biggest and busiest grocery store in Deer River, but it wasn't the only place in town that sold food. The Co-op store had a pretty good grocery selection too. And Bascum's general store had all the essentials.

Wally Conklin owned Bascum's, and while he had a fairly good line of hardware, he never tried to carry a big selection of food—just bread and milk, canned goods, pop and potato chips, that sort of thing.

"I never have any specials," he used to say. "Just having it makes it special here."

Wally bought his store from Arnold Bascum fifteen or twenty years before I was born, but never changed the sign above the front door, so people in Deer River never called it anything but Bascum's. Wally never painted the store either. From the time I can first remember seeing it, the outside walls were grayed from the weather.

Inside, everything seemed to be made from varnished, but well-worn, oak: a long L-shaped oak counter, oak floors, oak walls, and from the floor to the ceiling, oak shelves stocked with food, hardware, and various farm supplies. There was a big

pot-bellied woodstove that sat slightly to the rear of the middle of Wally's store. A couple of chairs, a nearby stool, and an eight-foot plank laid across the tops of two nail kegs gave his customers places to sit. The store was never crowded with people, but on cold winter mornings and rainy days during the rest of the year there were always a few men sitting around the stove. I doubt that business was any better for Wally on these days, though, since most of the men came to visit, not buy.

Unlike the conversation at Bert's, where social intercourse always seemed to be in high gear, the talk at Bascum's started slow—and sometimes it stayed there. Maybe it was because the kind of weather that forced men out of the fields and into town to places like Bascum's was also the kind that dampened conversation as well as the ground.

I remember a cold drizzly fall day when Pete Hawkins, Angus McKenzie, Joe Arnsted, Sparky Anderson, Wally, and a couple of other men sat around the fire and watched it rain. Most of the men had arrived at the store about the same time, and after exchanging greetings, had sat quietly, enjoying the warmth from the stove, and for the most part, losing themselves in their own thoughts.

After an unusually long silence, Angus McKenzie wiggled a little bit in his chair. "I was up to the cattle sale in New Cambridge last Saturday," he said. "Prices were low. One bunch of nice Hereford calves brought forty cents."

"Makes a man discouraged about the cattle business, don't it," said Pete.

"Depends on if you're buyin' or sellin'," said Sparky.

"You always got to sell them sometime," said Pete.

On that note the conversation stopped briefly. Sparky leaned over in his chair and spit tobacco juice into a tin can that sat on the floor below him. "You got any field work done this fall?" he asked Pete after he straightened up again.

"I was half through working up sixty acres on the home quarter when this started," Pete said, pointing at the rain falling against the front window. "I'm hoping winter won't come until I can get her finished."

"It'll probably turn cold after this rain," said Angus.

"It already is cold as far as I'm concerned," said Wally. Wally hated to go outside unless the temperature was above seventy degrees and he didn't have to go any farther than his car.

"We're lucky Jake isn't here," said Pete. "He'd tell us how cold it gets back in his part of Manitoba. He told me once that on a typical winter day if you threw a bucket of water out your back door it would freeze solid before it hit the ground."

"That's nothing," said Joe. "One day Jake told me that it was so cold up there that two or three times a winter the smoke would freeze and plug up the chimney."

Sparky said that Jake told him once about a day so cold a teakettle full of boiling water froze solid right on the stove. "Jake told me the whole thing happened so fast that when he picked up the kettle the ice was still warm."

"Jake was telling me about mosquitoes once," said Wally. "He said they were so thick back where he came from that you could swing a knife through the air and draw blood. He said they were so big that when one would land on a fence post it was easy to mistake it for a meadowlark."

"One time Jake told me that he saw a misquito so big it killed one of his cows," said Sparky. "He told me that he ran to the house to get the rifle, but before he could get back the mosquito had ate the cow and was standin' at the pasture gate ringin' the bell for the bull."

"Sounds to me like the bull was already there," said Angus.

The conversation stopped for a short time. Joe Arnsted finally put his hands behind the straps of his bib-overalls and said, "I still think the funniest thing Jake ever did or said was that day when he imitated Ernie Hoppingarner's wife Mildred.

"You remember how whenever Ernie was in the back room at Bert's playing cards Mildred would find out and come to the side door and yell for him to come home. Old Ernie would quit in the middle of a game sometimes if she caught him in there.

"Anyway, one day Jake and I were into Bert's and we happened to notice Ernie in the back room playing cards. When we left we turned down the lane on our way over here, but when we went by Bert's side door Jake stuck his head in and yelled, 'Now you come on home, Ernie.'

"You remember what a high-pitched voice Mildred had? Well, Jake sounded just like her. We kept walking, but pretty soon we looked back and there was Ernie out on the street with his hat in his hand scratching his head."

Sparky laughed longer and harder than anyone else at Joe's story, then leaned over and spit tobacco juice into the can on the floor. When he raised up Sparky said that Joe's story reminded him of something that happened one time in a beer parlor up in Hastings.

"This was fifteen or twenty years ago," Sparky said. "I was sittin' in this little place I don't even think is there anymore. I'd just stopped in for a beer while I was waitin' for a cattle auction up the road to start. Shorty Jacobs from over the other side of New Cambridge was in there too, waitin' on the same sale, so he can vouch for this story.

"It was a Saturday afternoon and this place was packed. Everybody was friendly, though, and we were all laughin' and tellin' lies to each other when all of a sudden I hear somebody shout, 'So there you are, you skinny little ignoramous!' I turned around and there was the biggest woman I'd ever seen standin' in the doorway. She probably weighed about 250 pounds and stood taller than I do.

"Well, I want to tell you that bar got so quiet you could hear her breathe clear across the room, and everyone was kinda lookin' around to see who the skinny ignoramous was. . . . Pretty soon this guy over in the corner—who was small although I wouldn't call him skinny—puts on his hat and gets up. He kinda smiled a nervous smile at us and said, 'Well, see you guys later.' Nobody said a word until both of 'em had left, but I think most of us were feelin' mighty relieved that we weren't the skinny little ignoramous she was after."

After Sparky's story Angus McKenzie asked the other men what happened to Shorty Jacobs that he never came around Deer River anymore.

"I don't believe I've seen Shorty over this way in ten years," Angus said, "although I guess I have seen him a time or two over in New Cambridge. Used to be you'd see Shorty over here quite a bit."

Sparky said that Shorty used to buy livestock regularly in Deer River. "He doesn't do much buyin' and sellin' anymore though," Sparky said, "so I guess he doesn't need to get over here much now. Shorty's gettin' up there in age you know. He must be eight or ten years older than I am, and I ain't no spring chicken. The years haven't been as easy on Shorty either."

Angus McKenzie leaned forward in his chair and said, "You know, one of the damndest stories I ever heard was about Shorty Jacobs. It happened fifteen or twenty years ago, maybe more. Shorty had some marshland property over around New Cambridge somewhere. It had a creek running right through the middle of it and so Shorty gets this idea that he could grow wild rice.

"He put a little money into the property and did some diking, and just about the time he got set up so he could seed some of this rice, he started having trouble with beavers. Shorty would no sooner get one beaver dam cleaned out of one place than he'd find that they'd been to work someplace else. And by the time he'd get the new dam cleaned up, the first one would be back in operation. The conservation people weren't any help because they said the beavers were there first.

"Shorty tried to deal with the critters the best he knew how, but nothing seemed to work. He tried trapping them, but there were too many. Then somebody told him that beavers will leave the area if you can give one of 'em a lickin'. I don't know why any such silliness would be true, but Shorty heard it someplace anyway and he decided to try it.

"He went out and rigged up some kind of trap, but I guess the first beaver he caught got killed in it somehow. The second time the trap worked better, though, and Shorty had a live beaver.

"And I guess he took that beaver and gave it a spankin'. Just turned him over his knee and spanked the varmint . . . but you know Shorty can't be much bigger than a full-growed beaver himself, and when he went to turn the animal loose the beaver knocked him into the water and Shorty damn near drowned. Now that's supposed to be a true story, but can you imagine such a thing as a grown man giving a beaver a spankin'. . . ."

"Well," said Sparky, "Shorty liked a drink of whiskey once in a while so maybe it's true, but one thing I know is that Shorty sold that land without ever plantin' any wild rice on it, so even if it is true, I think maybe the beaver got in the last lick."

Joe Arnsted began to laugh, and then said, "You know, that

story reminds me of another one Ralph told me about Shorty. He said that one time the Jacobs had an old tomcat they had to get rid of and so Shorty was sent to kill it. He was only about twelve years old.

"I guess they put the cat in a sack and Shorty took it down to the railroad bridge just outside New Cambridge. By the time he went to throw the cat off the bridge, though, the animal had kinda worked its way part way through a hole in the sack, and just as Shorty let go of the bag the cat reached out and clawed at his clothes trying to hang on.

"Those claws grabbing at him kinda surprised Shorty, and what with the force of trying to throw the bag and everything, he lost his balance and fell in the river too. Shorty told everybody afterwards that the cat beat him to shore."

After Joe's story Angus McKenzie pointed out the front window. "Do you know," he said, "I think it's going to quit raining."

"Maybe we can get some work done today after all," said Pete Hawkins.

Sparky leaned forward and spit tobacco juice at the can under his chair . . . and almost hit it.

Back in Manitoba

People in Deer River often said they'd like to visit Jake Peters's old home town because, they said, if even half of the stories Jake told about it were true the place would be a better choice for a vacation than Disneyland. Jake always said that it wasn't that people where he came from were any different from folks other places; it was just that the things they did always seemed to turn out a little different for them.

"Take old Maud Fisher, for instance," Jake said one day. "She lived alone on a farm about three miles from our place, and one spring she bought a little two-day-old Jersey calf. Every morning she'd come out and lift it over the fence so it could spend the day in the pasture. Then at night she'd lift it back over the fence again and put it in the barn. Now that's the kind of thing that can happen anywhere. I imagine the calf was heavy for old Maud to lift, but nobody thought anything about it at first because the calf didn't weigh too much and Maud was in pretty good shape for an eighty-year-old woman.

"Little by little, though, Maud got to be the strongest old woman anybody around home had ever seen. That calf just grew a little bit every day so I guess Maud never noticed the difference.

By the end of the summer, though, she was lifting a four-hundred-pound heifer over the fence twice a day; and by the next spring she was lifting a three-quarters-grown cow. By the time Maud was milking that Jersey, grown men were coming around to get Maud to help out whenever they had any heavy work to do.

"I remember one year back home," Jake said on another occasion, "when a bunch of us boys were sitting around Potts's General Store looking at a bunch of watermelons. Old Mr. Potts had just got them in. He had a couple of dozen all together, but there was one real big one. For a joke Mr. Potts says to Abe Jones that he'd bet him a dollar and a half that he couldn't eat the big melon in one sitting.

"Now, Abe Jones was known for having a big appetite and a small brain, but he was pretty careful with his money so he didn't take Mr. Potts up on the bet right away. He looked the melon over pretty careful, and then asked if he could think about it awhile and decide later. Mr. Potts told him that that would be fine with him.

"Abe left the store and went on home then, but in about half an hour he came back with a big grin on his face. 'Is that bet still on?' he asked.

" 'It sure is,' said Mr. Potts, and he brought Abe the big melon. It must have weighed about forty pounds, but Abe dug right in like he was used to eating melons that size. He ate for about fifteen minutes, but then began to slow down. Pretty soon it was obvious that he wasn't going to be able to finish. Mr. Potts said that he thought Abe ought to give up, but Abe kept trying.

"After a little while more, though, even Abe had to admit that he couldn't do it. 'I just don't understand it,' he told us. 'I just ate a melon at home that was bigger than this one and I didn't have any trouble with it.' "

One day at Bascum's Store Jake told about two brothers back in Manitoba.

"There used to be a pair of bachelor brothers who lived together on a farm up home," he said. "Their names were Ike and Mike Edmonds, and they got along pretty well until one time Mike bought a pet monkey.

"The cussed thing didn't pay much attention at all to Mike actually, but he thought the world of Ike. It liked to sit on Ike's lap all the time, and it followed him around the farm like a puppy. Ike couldn't hardly tolerate the monkey though. He said that it smelled like a sour dish rag.

"The more Ike complained about the animal, the more the monkey seemed to take to him. Mike wouldn't get rid of it, though, so before long the two brothers got so mad at each other they wouldn't even speak. The monkey just kept following Ike around, and after a while it got so it would copy everything he did. When Ike ate dinner the monkey would pick up a spoon and try to eat too. If Ike was combing his hair, the monkey would comb his. Ike said that if he went to the outhouse the monkey would try to get in and sit on the other hole.

"Ike told me that one morning, though, while he was shaving, he looked up and saw the monkey's reflection behind his own in the mirror. The monkey had Mike's straight razor, and he was copying everything Ike did.

"Ike brought his razor slowly down his right cheek. The monkey did the same. Then Ike drew the razor across his left cheek. The monkey did too. Ike smiled and pulled the back side of his razor quickly across the front of his neck in a straight line. The monkey did the same thing . . . but didn't turn the blade around. Ike said he never had any more monkey problems after that."

"I'll tell you a true story," Jake said one day. "It happened back home out on the provincial highway when I was a kid. See, what happened was that there was a woman and her son travelling by car through our area, and the little boy had a pet toad.

"Now this is a true story. The kid let the toad slip out of his hands, and it jumped onto the back of the woman's neck and slipped down her blouse. She pulled the car to the side of the road, jumped out screaming and shaking and flopping around trying to get this toad out of her clothes.

"An old guy named Maurice Manders was driving the next car to come along the road, and he happened to be coming from a first aid course the Department of Agriculture had put on over in the next town. When he saw the woman dancing around on the side of the road he figured she had taken a fit of some kind, and he jumped out of his car, grabbed her, and stuck a pencil in her mouth to keep her from swallowing her tongue. The woman put up quite a struggle, but Maurice expected that from what his instructors had told him.

"Benny Nasterly was in the next car that came along, and when he saw Maurice wrestling this strange woman to the ground he figured Maurice had gone berserk and was attacking her. He jumped out of his car and hit Maurice over the head with a ten-pound sack of potatoes he was bringing home from the store.

"By the time Maurice came to, half the town was out on the highway trying to figure out what had happened, and the woman and her little boy had already fled, vowing never to drive our particular stretch of highway again."

One day Pete and Sparky were talking about what poor memories they each had, and before long they were telling stories about people they had known who could remember details much better.

Jake listened to their tales for awhile, and then said, "You know, there used to be an old fellow up home, a carpenter by trade, who could remember everything he ever did if it related to his work. His name was Harry Mitchell, and that man could forget to put his shoes on in the morning sometimes, but if it was about carpentry he'd remember every detail. He could tell you about every square inch of every cabinet he had ever made, and he could tell you the exact dimensions of any building he had ever built.

"I worked for him one summer and the first day on the job I watched him measure a board with a carpenter's rule so old all the paint had worn off of it. 'My goodness, Mr. Mitchell,' I said, 'how on earth can you measure anything with that rule? All the marks have worn off of it.'

" 'Jake,' he said, 'I been using this rule so long I just always remember where they were.' "

The Old Days

Pete Hawkins was particularly fond of telling stories about the old days in Deer River. "The old stories beat anything I can make up," he'd say. One of the tales he used to tell was about the town's first doctor.

"Doc Sawyer came to town before I was born," Pete would say. "But I can remember him all right. He stayed here in Deer River right up until he retired and bought a cottage up on Lake Manitaugosis and started spending his winters in Florida. I believe he died down there. Course that was years ago now.

"Doc was quite a man. He never charged anybody for anything unless they got cured. I remember my dad telling how he went to old Doc Sawyer once a week for three months trying to get rid of a boil on the back of his foot. Doc never charged him for any but the last visit when he saw for sure the boil was going to go away.

"I can remember Doc saying that when he first came here to Deer River he had to stay open on Saturday nights to make enough money to keep from going broke. He said there was enough fightin' and carryin' on back then in Deer River to do a brisk business every Saturday night.

"Another thing I remember about Doc Sawyer. He had an old barn out behind his office where he kept chickens and pigs and other farm animals that he took as payment from people who might not have any cash money.

"One story I remember Doc telling was about when he first came to Deer River. Doc said he had just got out of school when he first came here and he looked pretty young to be a doctor. He said people in town didn't trust him at first because he looked like such a kid. Old Doc said he waited over two weeks to get called for his first case. It was a woman who lived about twelve miles out of town. I know the family well. They still live here.

"Anyway, she was going to have a baby, and when Doc got out there she was already pretty far along. Back then, back before Doc came to Deer River anyway, most women just had their babies at home, and when there was no doctor they were usually attended by older women with considerable experience in helping with births.

"And that's the way it was with Doc's first case. When he got there, there were two old ladies who had been called in for the birth too. They looked Doc up and down because he was so young, but they gave him his due because he had formal training, and they made it clear that he was in charge.

"When he asked them how the patient was doing they told him that she wasn't doing any too good. They said that it could be a tough birth and they felt he ought to 'snuff her'. Well, old Doc didn't want to look bad on his first case. Being so young was disadvantage enough with these two old ladies, so he didn't tell them that he didn't know how to snuff the patient, or, for that matter, that he didn't know what it was *to* snuff the patient. Doc just says to them, 'Well, I better see her first.'

"The two old women took him into the bedroom where the mother-to-be was in a considerable amount of pain. Doc said there wasn't really much he could do except wait for the baby to be born . . . and he was hoping that it would come soon so he wouldn't have to let on that he didn't know what it was to snuff somebody.

"The baby just didn't seem to want to come, though, and after a while one of the women asked if he didn't think he should snuff the mother. Doc tried to look thoughtful. It was getting well along in the evening, maybe nine or ten o'clock, and he says, 'Well, I guess if she hasn't had this baby by midnight we had better snuff her.' The old women nodded their heads in agreement, but it seemed to Doc that they thought he was making a mistake to wait so long.

"And the woman didn't make any progress. Doc just kept watching the clock while it got closer and closer to midnight. Finally it was twelve o'clock. Nobody said anything, but Doc knew the women were waiting for him to snuff the patient.

"Doc swallowed hard and then said, 'Now, you ladies look to me like you've had a lot of experience in matters of childbirth, and I'd like to have you snuff the patient now.'

"Doc said that right away those two women went to scurrying about getting ready. They got a can of Copenhagen from the expectant father and took a fingerful and blew it gently into the patient's nose. Two minutes later the woman sneezed. And five minutes after that she had her baby.

"Doc told the women they'd done an excellent job of snuffing, and nobody ever knew he hadn't known what it was they were going to do."

People in Deer River often talked about how much harder earlier generations worked, and how people were more honest in the early days.

"There used to be a story my dad told," Pete Hawkins said one day. "It was about Howard Jensen's grandfather. I can't remember now what his name was, but Howard's a grandfather now himself so you know it was a good many years back.

"Anyway, this Jensen, whatever his name was, was a fisherman in the wintertime. A lot of people fished through the ice back then—still do for that matter—but I think there were more in the early days. One year, when it was getting along towards spring, Jensen and a number of other men were caught on some floating ice up on Lake Manitaugosis.

"The way it happened was that the weather had been warm for several days, and the ice had broken apart in the center of the lake; but along the shore it still looked good, out for maybe a mile or so. Jensen had borrowed a team of horses to haul his ice house home.

"Nobody knew anything was amiss on the ice until they were

ready to come off the lake. When they got to where the shore should have been, there was ten feet of open water, and the ice was still floating away from the land. One of the men found a spot where a peninsula of ice made the shore five feet closer and everyone except Jensen jumped for it. They all landed in icy water, but it wasn't deep so they were able to get on dry land easily enough.

"Jensen, though, wouldn't leave the ice. All of the men called to him to jump, but he refused, and the ice was floating farther and farther out into the lake. See, Jensen had borrowed the horses and he wouldn't leave them. He floated on that ice all night and part of the next day. A strong north wind came up during the night and Jensen almost froze to death before it finally blew the ice against the shore fifteen miles up the lake from where he had originally intended to bring the horses off the ice.

"That kind of honesty just isn't around these days," Pete said. "People aren't like that anymore."

"Do you know," Pete said on another day, "at one time every quarter section around here—even the ones that by rights can't support a farm—had a family living on it. . . . And the first people who were here—the ones who came before the railroad—they had to walk the forty-five miles from Spruce Point where the tracks ended.

"Very few of the first settlers had horses, and even the ones who did, didn't get a lot of use out of them on the old Deer River trail. It ran through thick bush country along the side of the lake for most of the way. A good share of the year it was full of ruts and mudholes. Where it went onto the prairie, the grass was taller than a man's head.

"My mother's parents were one of the area's earliest settlers. They arrived late in the summer and spent their first winter in an old log barn that used to be on the Donald Arnsted place. I remember going to look at it with my mother when I was a little boy.

"My grandfather left for a while that first winter to work building the railroad that goes to Hastings, and my grandmother used to tell stories about living alone in that barn with two small children during the time he was away.

"She told about Indians coming to the door, and occasional

visits from neighbors who lived maybe three or four miles away. She said that my grandfather had left firewood stacked for her beside the barn, but late in the winter it dwindled to almost nothing, and he still wasn't home. One afternoon a blizzard blew up and my grandmother sat in that barn with what she figured was enough wood to last one more day. She guessed that if the storm lasted for more than that they would all freeze to death.

"The next morning there was nearly two feet of new snow on the ground, but the blizzard had stopped. She dressed the two children and started out on foot for the closest neighbors, which, like I said, would have been three or four miles away. She hadn't gone but a hundred yards or so, though, when she saw my grandfather coming home.

"See, Grand-dad had been forced to take shelter at a neighbor's because of the blizzard. Gramma said that when she first saw him across the field he was walking along on a pair of snowshoes like he was on a Sunday hike with not a care in the world. As soon as spring came, though, Grand-dad built a little house on the quarter he homesteaded, about a half mile from the log barn, and he started farming full-time. He said that after that winter away, and that blizzard, he never wanted to take railroad pay again. For the rest of his life he never did any kind of work except farming—and neither have any of his sons or grandsons."

Sometimes Pete told about some of the other early homesteaders in the Deer River district. One of his favorite stories was about a fellow named Sam Ryerdon. Ryerdon never did make a go of it on the land.

"He didn't know much about farming to begin with," Pete said, "but it was oxen that was his downfall. Most of the early homesteaders around here worked with oxen until they could afford a horse, but the beasts were somewhat difficult to manage and lots of people had trouble handling them.

"One time, so the story goes, this guy Ryerdon was trying to plow a field with his team, but he couldn't keep them to a straight furrow. He fought the animals for half the morning before he finally lost his temper, threw down the reins and yelled, 'All right, you sons-a-bitches, go where you want to! It's all got to be plowed anyway.' "

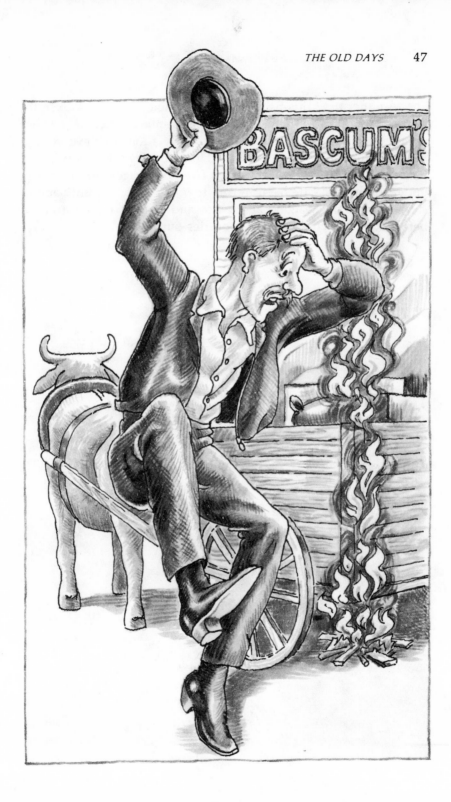

"Another time this Sam Ryerdon hitched his team of oxen to his wagon and took them to town for supplies. After he got the wagon loaded the oxen wouldn't move. Ryerdon tried everything he could think of to get them started, but nothing seemed to work. Finally he got so mad he got down from the wagon and lit a fire under the beasts. The oxen moved then all right, but only about six feet, and the wagon caught fire and burned to the ground before Ryerdon could get his groceries out."

The
Worst Year

The summer Harrison Walker sold out he held an auction sale at his farm half a dozen miles south of Deer River. Besides the array of tools, farm machinery, livestock, and household goods that are found at most farm auctions, Harrison owned a mammoth pile of old implement parts and scrap metal that he wanted to sell too. Over the years Harrison had collected enough old machinery to be thought of as Deer River's only junk dealer, even though his primary occupation had always been farming.

Everyone figured that there was so much to sell at Harrison's sale that it would last for two days—everyone, that is, except Charlie Connors, the auctioneer. Charlie said he'd sell everything before sundown. He started the sale at eight o'clock on a Saturday morning, selling the hand tools and garden implements first. At half-past ten he moved out into the yard and sold a couple of wagons, a granary, and two piles of used lumber.

By eleven o'clock he was moving to the household goods and it looked like he might be able to sell everything after all. Then thunder clouds started to build in the west and twenty minutes later it started to rain.

At first Charlie just kept right on selling. But then, after most of the people found shelter either in the house, one of the tool sheds, or a pole barn that was nearby, he decided to call an intermission in the sale while it rained. He had some of the men move the furniture that was left back into the house, and he put a tarp over the table with the kitchen ware and knick-knacks.

Pete Hawkins and Sparky Anderson were in the pole barn with about a hundred and fifty other people watching the storm. Pete said that Deer River needed a light rain to help the grain ripen. Sparky Anderson said that might be true, but it was really the last rain the town would need to see until after harvest.

Randolf McKenzie, who was standing next to Pete, said that while the rain couldn't hurt anything very much right then, it always bothered him to see storms when it was nearing harvest time.

"I've been farming for almost fifty years," Randolf said, "and the worst year I ever had was because of too much rain, not too little. I've seen it so dry you had to spit dust, but the worst year I ever saw was 1928. I would have been better off planting a rice paddy that year.

"Actually, the year started off pretty good, maybe even a little dry. Prices were not very good then, but better than they would be in the Dirty Thirties. At mid-season it looked like we were going to have a bumper crop, but then, before anything could get ripe, it started raining, and it kept raining for the rest of the summer. You know—some days rain, some days drizzle, some days just overcast, but never any sunshine for the grain. It didn't take long for a bumper crop to go bad.

"The wheat never developed the way it should—too much moisture, too little sun—and by fall half my fields were under water. Even if there had been fifty bushels to the acre there's no way I could have harvested it. You couldn't get on the fields. I waited until after freeze-up and then tried to cut the best of it, but the weather turned warm the first day out and before it froze again the snow came and buried everything. The next year I just plowed the whole thing up and started over.

"Do you know, all through the thirties there was never a year as disappointing as 1928. Oh, we had some bad years all right, but I'll always remember 1928 as the worst. Every day I'd look at the sky, but it would be the same thing. Towns all around here got some sunshine, but in Deer River all it knew how to do was rain. The next year it was dry, but we had enough moisture left over for everything to grow well anyway. Then came the Dirty Thirties and I wondered whatever happened to all the rain we had in 1928."

Pete Hawkins said that the worst year of farming he could remember was 1950. That was the year he had foot rot in his cattle herd, the price of cream fell to a new low, and an early frost hit his grain crop.

Sparky Anderson said that the worst year he ever had was 1946.

"That was the year I put everything I had into pigs," he said. "I had a big pasture all fenced with pig wire and there was a lot of good feed for them in it—acorns from the oak trees, lots of grass and legumes, plenty of bush to root around in. I had it all figured to be a pretty good year.

"The first half went along all right, too. I got my feeders for a pretty good price. I must have had 150 of 'em, and they seemed to do real well in the pasture. Of course, I was supplementing their feed with chop and some buttermilk I was able to scrounge from the creamery.

"By about mid-summer those pigs had pretty well ate the grass in the pasture down to nothing, and then along came a big thunderstorm. Well, I tell you, it must have rained about two inches worth of water in twenty-four hours, then it cleared up for a day or two, maybe three, and then it started to rain again. And it rained off and on for about a week. Turned the whole pasture into a gigantic mudhole.

"Of course, them pigs loved it. They got out there and rolled around in that gumbo mud just like it was a big swimmin' pool. After the rain the weather turned sunny and hot, and I guess them pigs could keep cool by layin' around in the mud.

"Anyway, after those big rains we didn't get any more moisture for the rest of the summer. And as hot as it was, it didn't take long for that pasture and all that gumbo mud to dry up.

"As you might expect them pigs was just covered in mud, and when it dried it shrunk and pulled them pigs' skin back as it caked along their sides. In fact, their skin was stretched so tight from the gumbo mud that it held their eyelids open. . . . And do you know, within two weeks ever' one of them pigs was dead. They died from lack of sleep. . . ."

After Sparky told his story the rain began to let up, and Charlie started the sale again. There wasn't time to sell everything that day before dark, though, so Charlie sold the livestock and some of the scrap metal the following morning. Everyone said that Harrison would have gotten a better price for many of the items if there hadn't been the delay. Sparky said he reckoned that year would be Harrison Walker's worst.

Out in the Country

Jake, Pete, and Sparky found special delight in rural life, but many of their stories emphasized, and often exaggerated, both its parochialism and its supposed lack of sophistication. Even though they told these stories in a spirit full of admiration for life in the backwaters of civilization, to avoid even a hint of ridicule towards their home town, they would usually make the locale for these stories somewhere other than Deer River.

Jake usually told his "country stories" about the place he came from in Manitoba. Pete and Sparky told their stories about Sparta, a little cross-roads village with a general store and a closed-down gas station that was the smallest town near Deer River.

It was generally agreed in our town that people in Sparta lagged behind the rest of the world in education and social behavior. One story told of a young man from the town who went up to Hastings and applied for a job in a shoe store. The owner of the store asked the boy if he knew anything about shoes.

"Well, I ought to," said the young man. "I've been awearin' 'em for six months."

People aren't so different from one place to another, though. They just have a little different point of view. For instance, there's

Pete's story about a city fellow who got fed up with urban life and one day, instead of going to work at his government office, got in his car and drove out into the country.

"He just kept driving and driving," said Pete, "and about noon he was hopelessly lost, running out of gas, and getting kind of hungry.

"Well, as luck would have it, the next town he came to was Sparta. He saw right off that there wasn't much there, just that old Esso gas station, Bartnik's store, and half a dozen houses all surrounded by good farmland. This was before the gas station went out of business, and he pulled up next to the pump.

"Old Ned Wilson owned the garage then, and you know how slow Ned walked. By the time he got out to the gas pumps the city fellow was out of the car waiting for him. He told Ned to fill the automobile with gas while he went across the street to get something to eat.

"Ned filled the car with gas all right, and was just finishing washing the windshield when the city fellow came back from the store eating an apple and a Twinkie. He was breathing the fresh air and just beaming at being out of the city. He looked up at the sky, and then said to old Ned, 'It sure must be nice living in the country.'

"Ned looked at him, then kinda smiled. 'Maybe,' he said, 'but I wouldn't know. I've lived here in town all my life.' "

Whenever anyone heard Pete tell that story it usually reminded them of the time old Ned had a Cadillac car stop at his station. The driver, a fat man who smoked a cigar, got out of the car while Ned filled the limousine with gasoline. The man surveyed Sparta and the surrounding countryside with a critical eye. "How on earth do people make a living in such a poor place?" he asked.

"Well, I can't speak for anybody else," Ned answered, "but I make mine selling gas to smart-talkin' tourists coming through here in fancy cars."

Sparky Anderson's favorite story about Sparta was true. At least everyone in Deer River said it was true. Back when the first telephones came into the area the first place around Sparta to get one was the local general store. A couple of days after they hooked it up there was a summer storm and eight or ten farmers were holed up in the store watching it rain when a local recluse named Clem came in. Now Clem had never seen or heard of a telephone, and he wouldn't believe anybody when they told him what it could do. "I ain't that big a fool," Clem told the men when they tried to convince him that he could talk to people in New Cambridge through the telephone.

When the men kept insisting that he could, Clem said, "All right then, my mother-in-law lives in Ashley and it's only half as far as New Cambridge. Let's see your talkin' machine work." The farmers made the call to the store in Ashley, and the folks there rustled up the old woman, but just as they handed the phone to Clem, a bolt of lightning hit the phone line outside the store. The shock threw Clem into the corner. When he got up he shook himself off and said, "Well, that's mom all right."

Jake Peters would never allow anyplace to seem farther into the backwoods than the area he came from in Manitoba.

"Why, we were so far out in the bush," he would say, "that the daily paper was always a year old before it would get to us, and we had to order our haircuts from the catalog. I can remember the very first circus to ever come to our town. It caused so much excitement they're probably still talking about it. See, one of the elephants escaped the day before the first show. It was a small circus with only one elephant, so most people never did get a chance to see the animal. The darn thing escaped during the night so nobody even saw it run off. By the time the circus people noticed it was gone it was so far into the bush that it didn't look like they'd ever find it.

"For three days there wasn't a trace of that beast, but then it turned up on the edge of a settlement even farther into the bush than we were. It seems this woman happened to look out of her kitchen window and here was that elephant out in her garden eating vegetables.

"Well, she ran out of the front door of the cabin and into the fields to get her husband. 'Come quick,' she yelled when she found him, 'I think one of those circus animals has escaped, and he's in our garden right now pulling up vegetables with his tail.'

" 'Pulling up vegetables with his tail?' her husband asked. 'What on earth is he doing with them?'

" 'Honey,' the woman answered, 'you wouldn't believe it.' "

Moonshine

Harry Doyle lived alone on a small place west of Deer River. He was a short man with only a few strands of long gray hair on his head and a half-inch stubble of beard on his face that never seemed to get shaved or grow into a proper beard.

Whenever people told stories about moonshine in our town, sooner or later they would talk about Harry. Sparky Anderson had worked for Harry for two summers when he was a teenager, so he knew the most stories about him.

"Mostly I just picked stones for Harry," Sparky said, "or did any other kind of work around there that Harry didn't want to do himself. Old Harry would get me to help him with his still once in a while, though.

"You know, that man would eat a bale of hay if somebody poured whiskey on it, and sometimes when he'd get to samplin' a run too much he'd get me to come into the old barn where his still was and I'd sit with him. He'd keep drinkin' until he fell asleep, and then it would be my job to keep his pot at the right temperature to finish off however many gallons he was cookin'.

"Harry told me one time that he used to have a brother who lived over the other side of Layton Corners. Harry used to live over there too. I think that was where he was raised. He and this brother used to make whiskey together. Harry told me they were a pretty wild pair when they were younger. Claimed they used to get into all kinds of devilment.

"One story Harry told me was about this game they used to play. Harry said they'd get a gallon jug of this home-brew they made and go to the barn where they'd each drink half of it. Then, Harry said, one of them would crawl off and the other one would try to guess which one it was.

"Another thing I always remember about workin' for Harry was the way he'd cuss at me whenever he went out the barn door. See, when I was just a little kid, way before I ever worked for him, I had carved my initials on the inside of that door, and Harry never passed it without cursing me. At least he never did when I was around to hear. He never made a big deal out of it; he'd barely look up. But he'd always say, 'By damn you, Sparky!' on his way past the door.

"Those two summers I worked for him I bet he went out the barn door a dozen times a day, and ever' time he'd swear at me. I bet he'd do it today if I'd go over there.

"After I was grown I used to go over to see old Harry once in a while to buy a little of his moonshine. Harry hated it if anyone called him a bootlegger. He didn't mind being called a moon-shiner, but he absolutely couldn't tolerate anyone callin' him a bootlegger. 'A bootlegger is just someone who sells whiskey,' Harry'd say. 'I make it. That's a lot different.'

"I don't think Harry ever thought about whiskey-makin' as bein' against the law, except for the obvious precautions he took so he wouldn't get caught. Harry just figured the government must have went wrong somewhere way back when they passed a law sayin' a man couldn't make his own liquor. And I guess I kind of agree with him on that. Harry has never hurt anybody with the whiskey he makes.

"Anyway, like I was sayin', I used to go see Harry once in a while when I got older, not as old as I am now, but old enough to be old enough, but still young enough to be rambunctious. . . . And Harry wasn't so old that he wouldn't make an occasional gallon of moonshine.

"One afternoon me and Hap Johnson decided to stop by

Harry's place. You know Hap was always willin' to take a drink. Somebody told me once there were only two things Hap Johnson would never do. He'd never talk about anybody behind their back, nor refuse a drink of whiskey.

"Anyway, when we got to Harry's there was no one around, so I figured he'd probably be down at his still. He had an old run-down barn on the other side of the quarter where he used to make liquor back then. It was the same place where I used to keep the mash boiling for him those summers I worked there.

"This old barn, it wasn't much bigger than a granary really; it sat back in the spruce trees where you couldn't see it unless you knew it was there. Coming across the field from the house you'd come up to the back side of the barn. On the other side was that slough that used to go for two miles or so across the Barrett place before they drained Higgons Lake.

"Hap didn't even know where Harry's still was, and he'd been to Harry's more times than I had. I was tellin' him about the barn on the way across the field and we got this idea to play a trick on old Harry.

"When we came up on the barn Hap went into the spruce trees on one side and I went into the trees on the other. Then we started shoutin' to each other, coverin' our mouths with our handkerchiefs so Harry wouldn't recognize our voices. 'Stay right there,' Hap yelled. 'He's over here,' I called back. 'He's in the barn.' It sounded like Harry was surrounded by an army. I didn't see him go, but I heard the door slam and knew there was only one direction for him to run—right across that old slough.

"Well, Hap and I didn't know what to do then. For a while we could hear poor Harry out in the swamp grass wading that marsh. Then we didn't hear anything so we went back to the house and got one of Harry's bottles and sat in his kitchen to drink it. We thought the whole thing was pretty funny, all right, but at the same time we were kind of worried that the joke had got out of hand, too. Neither one of us figured Harry for believin' the law was really after him—least not for more than a minute or two.

"The bottle was near gone before Harry ever came home. I guess he waited for it to get dark before he chanced comin' out of the bush. He was mostly dry by then, but he smelled like swamp water, and his pant legs were all stiff at the bottom and stained so you could tell he'd been wading in dirty water up to his thighs.

"Hap and I were pretty scared what Harry'd do to us, but he never said a word, never let on there was anything unusual that happened. So Hap and I never said anything either. After a while we paid Harry and left. Then we laughed about the whole thing. And we've laughed a time or two since then, too, but we never did tell Harry, and he's never said a thing more about it either."

Pete Hawkins had a story about Harry Doyle's moonshine too. Actually, it was about Josh Peterson and what happened when he drank some of Harry's brew one time. Peterson ran the local hardware store. He was tall and thin, about fifty years old with all gray hair that made him look rather distinguished.

Compared to most other people in Deer River at least, Josh Peterson had a rather reserved manner. People used to tell about the time Josh sat next to Maud Engles at a community supper. Maud was normally as talkative as Josh was reticent, and all through the meal she talked even faster than she normally did. Josh, meanwhile, tried as best he could to ignore her without appearing rude. That's the way Josh handled any trying situation—by ignoring it.

Finally, just before the meal ended, Maud turned to Josh and said, "You know, Josh, I made a five-dollar bet with my husband that before the meal ended I could make you say more than three words in succession. Since I've not succeeded yet, do you think you could help me out a little by just saying something?"

Josh thought for a minute and then said, "You lose."

Pete said the time Josh drank some of Harry's moonshine he was in Woody's barbershop.

"Josh was waiting for a haircut when George Arnsted and my cousin Bruce came in with a bottle from Harry Doyle's," Pete said. "Now, you know Woody Blackburn likes a drink of whiskey as much as anyone in town, and Don Dupris was in the chair, and Don always likes a bit of home-brew, so they all got to passing that bottle around the barbershop. Josh couldn't very well make an excuse for not being sociable since he was just sitting there waiting for his haircut. He took a drink when it came his turn just like everybody else.

"Bruce told me Josh always said thank you real politely—just like he had been passed the potatoes at some fancy dinner party—whenever someone handed him the bottle. Then he'd wipe the mouth of the bottle with his hand before he took a swallow. He drank as much as anybody else, though. Bruce said Josh wasn't afraid to tip the bottle up.

"Anyway, Josh stayed in the barbershop and drank whiskey until his haircut was finished; then he left and went home. There was a little whiskey left in the bottle so everybody else stayed in the shop. They watched Josh through the front window as he got in his car and drove away. It was right after Josh got his new Oldsmobile, the big 88 he had. It was a fine car, but after he drove off Woody says, 'Do you know, I don't think that was Josh's car.'

"Bruce said, 'Sure it was,' but Woody told him that Josh was walking when he came in. 'Mabel Maxwell has a new car just like Josh's,' Woody said, 'and I think he drove off in hers.'

"And that's just what happened. Josh drove Mabel Maxwell's car home, pulled up to his garage, got out, and opened the door—and there sat his own car in the garage where he had left it. Clayton Powell was across the street and he watched the whole thing.

"In Josh's condition, suddenly having two cars was too much to handle. He looked at one car, then the other one, but the more he looked the more confused he became, so he threw up his hands and went into the house and got into bed.

"And that's where he was when Mabel showed up looking for her car."

Jake Peters said that that story reminded him of the night Wade Phillips got his coat mixed up with someone else's over in New Cambridge. "We were over there for a bonspiel," said Jake, "and afterwards we had a few drinks at the hotel. I guess we stayed pretty late, but I don't remember closing the place down or anything.

"Wade had just bought a new fur coat. You know he can't be much more than five feet tall, and he looked like a little round ball of fur in that jacket.

"Anyway, there was a place to hang your coat where you first come in the door of the bar, and when Wade left, there was a coat that looked just like his that he took by mistake. I don't know why nobody noticed it then, but the next morning my doorbell rang and here was little Wade standing on the porch in this fur coat about six sizes too big. It hung to his ankles and he could slap the sleeves around like flippers.

"He wanted me to drive him over to New Cambridge to see if we could find whose coat he had. I told him that he might just as well keep the new coat since it was just like the old one anyway, but he said he couldn't do that 'cause he had somebody's car keys in the front pocket. That just made me laugh more. If he could have found someone as small as he was to get in there with him, Wade could have played a game of ping-pong inside that coat.

"When we got to the hotel in New Cambridge there was just one car out front—and both of us knew who it must belong to. Wade's coat was still inside hanging where he had left it. The bartender told us the guy whose coat we had was so big he couldn't even get Wade's coat on his back. He told us where the guy lived and we drove out there. The fellow turned out to be a big tall guy who weighed about 250 pounds. Wade said he was glad the guy wasn't mad at us, but I corrected him and said, 'At you, Wade. He'd be mad at you.' "

Sparky Anderson had a favorite drinking story that he liked to tell.

"You know," he'd say, "it hasn't been that many years ago when you'd go to a dance or social around here and there would be a cream can full of home-brew in the center of the room with a ladle hangin' on it for fillin' your glass.

"I remember a dance over at the old Hillcrest School that had a couple of cream cans full of Harry Doyle's. You can mix good home-brew about three to one with water and still have a pretty stiff drink, and one of the cans was toned down just a little bit.

"Early in the evenin', when not too many people had even had a drink yet, I was standin' out by the cream cans with Tom Hannah. We'd each had a couple of snorts already when Tom reached for the dipper to get another drink from the can on the right. 'Just a minute there, Tom,' I said. 'I think that's the weaker whiskey you've got there.'

" 'Don't be aworryin' about that,' Tom said. 'We're goin' to drink both of 'em.' "

Jake Peters told a story about the first time he ever went to a dance where they had home-brew.

"It was over in the next town from where I grew up," Jake said. "Kind of a rival town to ours actually. And it was just like here, a cream can of home-brew in the middle of the floor at a dance. Normally I wouldn't have been to any kind of social gathering in this town, but I liked a girl over there so came to this dance. When I came to the door, though, one of them town boys looked at me kind of mean. He must have decided I was all right, though, because he took that dipper they had and filled me a big glass of this moonshine.

"Now up to this point I hadn't been a drinker. I hadn't been old enough very long. I said, 'No thank you. I don't believe I'll have any.'

"Well, that fellow reached over and grabbed a ball bat he had with him, looked at me kind of menacingly, and said, 'Now I asked if you didn't want a drink.'

"I told him that since he put it that way I was going to reconsider. He gave me a glass, and I downed it in one shot. Well, my whole insides turned to fire and I fell right on my face in the middle of the dance floor.

"When I got up the fellow says, 'How was it?'

" 'Pretty good, I guess,' I told him.

" 'That's fine,' he said. 'Now here's the ball bat. Make me drink some of it.' "

More Talk about the Weather

Anybody in Deer River who could remember more than twenty-five or thirty winters maintained that the temperatures were gradually moderating. Everyone had a story about how the winters were colder, longer, and had more snow when they were younger.

Jake Peters didn't pay any attention to these stories. He said that even if Deer River was twice as cold it would still be the banana belt compared to the winters he spent when he was a boy. Jake admitted to some cold Deer River mornings, though. In fact, he had a bigger selection of cold temperature sayings than anyone else in town.

"It's so cold the dogs had to use jumper cables to start the rabbits," he'd say sometimes. Or, "It's cold enough to freeze an egg on the sidewalk." Or, "It's colder than an outhouse in the territories." Often his comparisons were less delicate.

Jake told a story one time about the autumn he asked Tom Hannah what kind of winter Deer River should expect. "Tom looked kind of thoughtful for a minute," Jake said. "Then he offered that it could be a pretty mild one. Tom doesn't like to commit himself, though. After another minute he says, 'Then again, it could be a pretty hard one.' Tom studied the matter a minute more. Then he said, 'We'll know come spring.' "

Pete Hawkins liked to tell the story about the summer of 1933 when, he said, the land around Deer River was the driest in recorded history. "It was so dry," Pete said, "that the grasshoppers sat around waiting for the wheat to come up for so long they starved to death."

"That's right," Sparky Anderson said. "One drop of rain fell from the sky all summer and it hit a neighbor of mine on the forehead. It took three buckets of sand to revive him."

"It was so dry we had to soak the pigs in the creek for a week before they would hold slop," said Pete.

"And hot," Sparky returned. "It was so hot my thermometer boiled dry."

"I know it," Pete said. "I had planted popcorn that year and it all popped right in the field. It looked like we had had a snow storm in July, and a couple of chickens of mine saw it and froze to death."

"And do you remember how windy it was that year?" Sparky asked. "Why the wind was so strong it blew a pig of mine into a gallon jug."

"Yea, you talk about the weather," said Pete. "But they just don't have weather anymore like they used to."

Fishing
Stories

Some people think tall tales started with exaggerated fishing stories. Jake Peters always said that fishermen were such notorious liars he automatically took three pounds off the weight of any fish he heard about.

Jake said that he told a fishing story to Tom Hannah one time, and when Hannah didn't seem impressed with the size of Jake's fish, Jake asked, "What's the matter, Tom? Don't you think that's a lot of fish?"

Hannah didn't say anything for a minute and then answered, "No, I think that's a lot of bull."

One time Pete Hawkins came into Bert's telling about catching a nine-pound pickerel at Round Lake, a small body of water only a little bigger than a pond out near his farm. Everybody in Deer River knew there hadn't been fish that size in that lake since the government dammed a creek between it and Sand Lake fifteen years before, but nobody said anything to Pete.

He went on to tell how he had been fishing on the same lake three years earlier and had caught a pickerel too small to keep. "I threw him back," Pete said, "but before I did, I cut three notches out of his tail. Now the funny thing is that this fish I caught last night has three notches cut out of his tail too, so I think it's the same fish."

Adding the little twist about the notches in the tail gave Pete's story some credibility. Most people were turning the matter over in their minds when Jake spoke up.

"You know, Pete," he said, "I'll bet that was the same fish you caught before. That kind of thing happens all the time. I remember one time when I was fishing up on Lake Manitaugosis. It was nearly dark and I was letting the boat drift with the current, half trolling. I was thinking about quitting so I pulled my watch out of my pocket to see what time it was and bamm, a jackfish struck my lure. Well, I grabbed at my rod and knocked my watch out of the boat. There was nothing I could do except watch it sink out of sight.

"About a year later I was fishing in about the same spot with a big heavy old red and white spoon. I let out too much line and the spoon got caught up in some weeds on the bottom. When I pulled it back to the boat I found that I'd snagged my own watch."

Jake paused. "The amazing thing about that incident was that the watch was still ticking—and gave the correct time."

Everybody laughed, then Pete said, "I'll tell you what, Jake. I'll take three pounds off my fish if you'll stop that watch."

The sign on the front of the building said Bert's Cafe, but Bert's was more than the name suggested. Besides serving modest lunches, providing card and pool tables for recreation, and establishing itself as a local meeting hall, Bert's was also the only bait shop in Deer River.

Bert didn't sell a lot of tackle, but you could buy a fishing license there, along with red worms, night crawlers, and minnows. In season, Bert kept his supply of worms next to his ham sandwiches and soda pop in the refrigerator.

Because he sold bait, there was probably an inordinate amount of discussion at Bert's built around the angler's art. One day, after a series of how-I-caught-the-biggest-fish stories, Paul Kelly topped them all with a true one.

Kelly, who was about forty, farmed a section of land about halfway between Deer River and New Cambridge. He didn't tell many stories, but when he did they were straight-forward ones, as honest as Kelly was in his business dealings. That's why everyone was surprised at the circumstances of the tale.

"Now, you've been telling some mighty big yarns," Kelly began, "but I want to tell you about the biggest fish I ever caught. I'm a bit ashamed of the whole episode really, but it has been nearly thirty years now since it happened and it is kind of funny.

"You all know about the Austin Fish Festival up at Lake Barega. Well, my mother grew up in Austin and my brother and I used to spend part of every summer there staying with my grandparents when we were young.

"One year when I was about eleven and my brother was fifteen we were in Austin while they had their fish derby, so naturally John and I entered. The way the thing worked then was that you registered on Friday afternoon and the person who brought in the biggest fish by Sunday at six o'clock in the evening won the prize.

"John and I didn't have a boat like most of the contestants, but we fished from shore and off the piers pretty steady all weekend. We often caught fish up there when we stayed with my grandparents, but this particular weekend we didn't catch a thing. Sunday came and neither one of us even had a fish to enter for a prize, let alone win anything.

"We fished together in the morning, and then my grandfather came out with a picnic lunch for us at noon. We ate it up on a hill overlooking the lake at a beach where we used to swim. It was a favorite spot of ours then, and now it's part of the park they have up there.

"After lunch my grandfather left us, and John and I just lay around for a couple of hours before we went back to fishing. John got going before I did and started up the lake to a little tributary. I told him I was going to go around the lake the other way, try to see if I could get something along the west shore. We agreed to meet back at my grandparents' house before we went up town that evening.

"After John left I just lay on the beach for a while watching sea gulls, then I started back up the lake along the west shore. I was kind of disgusted with fishing by that time and was really just fooling around.

"I came to a little point of land that jutted out into the lake with open water on one side and lily pads pretty thick on the other. It had a bit of a beach there so I waded out for a ways off the point trying to land my bait just in front of the lily pads.

"There weren't any fish biting there either, but while I was standing there up to my belly in water, a dead pike came floating past me. I reached out, grabbed it and hauled it up on shore.

"I'd never seen a fish like it, and I still haven't to this day. It was huge, as long as I was. It must have died from old age because there wasn't a mark on it. It was fresh too. I decided to take it to show my grandfather.

"When I got to the house there was nobody there so I curled that old fish into a washtub in the back yard, left my fishing gear there beside it, and went down to a cousin's house where I thought my grandparents might be visiting. Well, there was nobody home there either, so I returned to my grandparents' house.

"When I got back my fish was missing. I couldn't figure out why anyone would steal a dead fish, but I knew the thing didn't run away on its own. There was nothing I could do about it, though, so I just sat around the house waiting for my brother to come back.

"And in a little while in he came. 'Paul,' he said, 'hurry up and get downtown. That fish of yours is going to win.'

"I didn't know what he was talking about for a minute, but of course what had happened was that John had got home while I was gone, found my fish, and entered it in the contest because he thought I didn't know enough to do it myself. When I told him how I got that fish both of us were scared, but John said that, in a way, I did catch it, and besides, we couldn't do anything about it because it was already entered.

"We went back downtown, and of course, my fish won the contest. I was the unhappiest lucky winner you ever saw. Everyone thought I was just shy, but the truth was I was scared to death somebody was going to come along and say they saw me drag that old dead fish out of the water. I think John was just as unhappy about the whole thing as I was, but he managed to act happier. My prize was a Kodak box camera. I gave it to my grandmother.

"Do you know it was weeks before people stopped talking about that fish. It seemed like months. I even got my picture in the Austin paper. At the end of the summer I was glad to get home and go back to school. And as far as I know, that fish still holds the record as the biggest ever caught at the Austin Fish Festival."

One morning Sparky Anderson brought a fish into Bert's that he'd caught up on Swan River. It was a beautiful pike that was well over two feet long, and everybody in the restaurant was impressed with it and told Sparky they were. Bert put it on his hamburger scales and it weighed just over thirty pounds.

"Not a bad fish, eh boys?" Sparky said.

Jake Peters said it was pretty good, but he had caught one bigger.

"Oh, really," Sparky said. "And how much did yours weigh?"

"Well, I don't know exactly," Jake said. "I never was able to find a set of scales big enough to weigh it, but when I pulled it into the boat the lake receded about a foot and a half."

Walter Maxwell was known as the biggest poacher around Deer River. People attributed him with taking fish and game in countless novel and unsporting ways. Some of the stories they told about Walter were true, but a lot of them nobody really believed. It's just that Walter's unconventional ways made him an easy place to hang a story.

One thing people used to laugh about was true, though. Walter's sister Betty married Lewis Kempton, the local game warden. There wasn't anyone in Deer River who couldn't see the humor in that.

Not long after they were married the story went around town how Lewis had gone fishing with Walter. There was a little lake that came up to the back end of Walter's property, and according to the story, Walter took Lewis out in his pontoon boat one Sunday. Lewis knew about Walter's poaching and before they left the dock he checked to see that Walter had a fishing license.

When the two men got out on the lake, though, Lewis realized he had made a serious mistake coming fishing with his brother-in-law. Walter didn't have any fishing tackle. "I figured since we were related now," he told Lewis, "I would teach you to fish the way I do."

With that Walter reached into his pocket, took out a quarter stick of dynamite, lit the fuse, and tossed it into the lake. There was an underwater explosion, and almost immediately, dead fish came floating to the surface.

Lewis was so flabbergasted he didn't know what to say at first. Finally he got himself together enough to stammer something about being the game warden, that he had responsibilities, the law was the law, and brother-in-law or not he would have to arrest Walter. "The law is bigger than any one person," Lewis said.

Walter wasn't paying any attention to Lewis's jabbering, however. He just lit another quarter stick of dynamite and handed it to his brother-in-law. When Lewis stopped talking long enough to see what he had in his hand Walter said, "See here, Lewis. Are you going to talk or fish?"

Sparky Anderson liked to fish as much as anybody in Deer River. He liked to say that the good Lord made the earth two-thirds water and one-third land because he intended people to spend one-third of their time working and two-thirds of their time fishing.

One morning Sparky came into Bert's with a sorrowful look on his face. It wasn't genuine moping, though. It was the kind of look that Sparky always got when he told one of his hard luck stories. Pete Hawkins called these tales "Poor Sparkies."

After he fixed himself a cup of coffee Sparky started his oration.

"I've been fishin' for over forty years," he said, "but last night was the worst fishin' I've ever had in my life. It's not that I didn't catch any fish. That wouldn't bother me none. I've been fishin' lots of times without catchin' fish. But last night I went three and a half hours and didn't even get my line in the water.

"See, I've been watchin' the fishin' up on Mulfree Lake for a couple of weeks now, and there's been a lot of activity startin' a couple of hours before the sun goes down. I've seen some pretty big fish breakin' the surface up there just before it gets dark. I even fished from shore a couple of evenin's and did all right.

"Last night I decided to take my boat and see what I could do. I put her in up by the beach at Bennett's Road, then rowed across to the marrow shallows up on the lake's northeast shore.

"Twenty yards from the lily pads I pushed the oars into the

mud to hold the boat steady, and went to the bow to get my gear ready. Last night was a really pretty evenin' and I could hear the slap of fish tails against the water.

"My rod was standin', wedged between the front seat and the point of the boat. I got a big old Hoola-Popper out of my tackle box and had just snapped it onto my leader when a mosquito landed on my neck.

"Well, I let go of the Hoola-Popper and slapped at the mosquito, but my hand swiped the fishhook on its way by. It caught me in my little finger between the joints. It hurt like hell, but the worst part was that my fishline was locked in the reel and the rod was wedged in tight, so my hand snapped back without killin' the mosquito.

"I must have been a pretty sight standin' there in the boat with my hand caught like that. My rod is nearly seven feet tall so I had to keep my hand raised above my head. I couldn't reach the reel to release the line, and I couldn't lift the rod from where it was wedged because it would pull on my hooked finger. To make matters worse the wind came up and blew the boat away from the oars out into the lake. And me, I'm standin' there in the front of the boat salutin' the sky and not able to do a thing.

"And the mosquito, of course, is still on my neck tryin' to bite me. By this time I was too mad to think straight and took another swing at the damn thing. The hook went deeper into my finger, but the line still kept me from killin' the mosquito. I only missed him by about an inch and a half, though, so I made another attempt.

"This time I swung with all the power I could muster, but of course never came close to killin' the mosquito. I just drove the hook deeper into my finger. About this time I figured out that my whole effort was backwards. I reached up and slapped the mosquito with my other hand.

"The boat was pickin' up speed as it sailed across the lake, and I had to figure out some way to release myself from the hook and line. I reached into my pocket, got my jackknife, and opened it with my teeth. By this time I was so mad that I'd completely quit using my head. I took a swipe at my line with the knife, but I used the back side of the blade so the jackknife snapped shut on my thumb. I tried again and cut myself free.

"Now, I'm out in the middle of the lake, the wind is blowin' me in the wrong direction, and I don't have any oars. You know how many people usually fish on Mulfree Lake. Well, last night there wasn't a soul. I got an old bait can and tried to use it for an oar, but it was no good. I tried paddling with my hands. The boat still went where it wanted to.

"Finally, after about an hour and a half on the lake, the wind drove the boat into that swampy area at the south end of the lake. The water was still up to my waist, but I walked the boat through the weeds until I got to where it was too shallow for it. I had to beach it there—and leave my rod and tackle box too. I walked out of the swamp and back to the car. I figure it's about three miles, and by that time it's pitch dark with grass up to my armpits and mosquitoes the size of hummin' birds tryin' to carry me away."

After a pause, Sparky said, "The worst part is that I have to go back out there today and find my boat so I can go fishin' with Blake Peterson tonight."

Charlie
Maystead

Charlie Maystead was only thirty-five when I left Deer River. While he wasn't old enough to be deemed a local character yet, it was generally agreed that, next to Tom Hannah's, his was the fastest wit in a town where snappy comebacks were admired and often repeated.

"Charlie was like that from the time he was a little boy," Pete Hawkins said. "I remember one time on the way out to Boscum's old place I saw him walking along the edge of the road. He couldn't have been any more than about eight years old, but he looked like he was on his way home from somewhere and was walking at a good pace, so I stopped to give him a lift. I don't know if you remember Clyde Boscum, but he was a dirty old cuss with about twelve or fifteen unkempt little kids that used to run all over the countryside.

"For a joke, when I come up to little Charlie on the road I leaned out the window and said, 'Oh, it's you Charlie. I guess I made a mistake here. See, I thought you were one of Clyde Boscum's boys.'

"Well, Charlie didn't hesitate even a second. He just looked me right in the eyes and said, 'Well, I guess that makes two of us that made a mistake then, 'cause I thought you was Clyde.' "

Sparky Anderson said that one time when Charlie was about fourteen he worked baling hay out at Mac Arnsted's place. "You know how tight Mac is," Sparky said. "Back then he'd have a couple of hired kids workin' in the hay mow and any time there wasn't a wagon in from the fields with a load of hay for them to be unloadin' and stackin' in the barn he'd dock the kids' pay for the time they didn't have anything to do.

"Charlie worked for Mac in the mow that summer, and when Mac brought the boys in for the noon meal one day he says to 'em, 'Now don't be afraid of those potatoes, boys. Dig right in.'

"Charlie kinda chuckled and says, 'Why, don't you worry, Mr. Arnsted, that little bit of potatoes would never scare me.' "

Jake Peters told a story about a time when Charlie came into his shop to kill some time waiting for the post office to open.

"I'd just finished welding a piece of steel pipe for Harvey Taylor's manure wagon when Charlie walked in," Jake said. "I'd laid the pipe on the bench to cool and was doing something else so I didn't see Charlie reach to pick it up until it was too late to warn him.

"He grabbed the pipe with one hand, and then dropped it back on the bench. I could see the surprise in his eyes and he was shaking his fingers. I laughed and said, 'Burnt you, didn't it?'

Charlie didn't hesitate a second. 'No,' he said. 'It just don't take me very long to look at a piece of pipe.' "

"Another time," Jake said, "I was over at Charlie's in the evening and he drank a half a dozen cups of coffee while I was there. I said to him, 'My goodness, Charlie, doesn't all that coffee keep you awake?'

" 'It helps,' Charlie said."

Dick Butler told about a night when he and Charlie had sat in the Deer River Hotel until closing, and then made a couple of stops after that. "It wasn't the smartest thing for me to do," Butler said. "I was working at the creamery over in New Cambridge at that time and I had to leave for work about 4:30 every morning. Charlie wasn't married then; he was still living out at the farm with his folks, so when it finally came time to go home I told him, 'Listen, it's already pretty late. Instead of me driving you home now, why don't you spend the night at my house and I'll take you home on my way to work in the morning.' Maysteads' was on the way to New Cambridge anyway.

"Well, Charlie thought that would be all right; he was in an agreeable mood. I fixed him a bed on a sofa we had on the back porch, but by the time we got to bed it was already about 2:00 A.M.

"A little after 4:00 I came out and shook Charlie awake. He swung his feet out onto the floor and rubbed his eyes. 'Damn,' he said. 'It sure don't take long to stay all night with you, does it?' "

Sparky Anderson said that one time he was out at his cousin Lloyd's place with Charlie. "Lloyd had bought some adjoining farmland over the winter," Sparky said, "so I guess he was feelin' pretty proud of his ranch. 'I've been out checkin' fences,' Lloyd said when we drove up, 'and do you know it takes me half a day now to drive around this place in my pickup.'

"I could see the sparkle in Charlie's eyes. 'I know what you mean, Lloyd,' he said. 'I've got a pickup truck like that at home, too.' "

Sparky told another story about Charlie Maystead.

"I went to see Charlie one fall," Sparky said. "He was just bringin' a gunny sack full of potatoes in from the garden. He was goin' to take them to the basement, I guess. Anyway, I asked him how the potato crop had turned out. 'Not too good,' Charlie said. 'I planted a bushel, and harvested a bushel.'

" 'That's too bad,' I said. 'How come you got so few?'

" 'It was my own fault,' said Charlie. 'I should have planted more.' "

Jake Peters said he saw Charlie in Josh Peterson's hardware store one autumn day and asked him if he wanted to go duck hunting. "What for?" asked Charlie. "I ain't lost no ducks."

One of Pete Hawkins's favorite stories about Charlie was about the time they were up at the feed mill in New Cambridge. "There was a guy there we got to talking to," said Pete, "who was telling us how tough it was to be old. 'I wouldn't know about that,' said Charlie, 'but I figure gettin' old ain't so bad when you consider the alternative.' "

Two More Stories

There were all different kinds of tales told in Deer River. Sometimes people made stories from simple incidents from their daily lives; sometimes stories were merely spoken yearnings or reflections.

One day in Trompkin's Store Mary Arnsted got to telling everyone about her sons. Both of them had graduated from high school in Deer River and both went on to get university degrees. Tom, the oldest, lived in the East and worked for a big chemical company. Benny lived on the west coast and taught at a university.

Mrs. Arnsted told everyone about her sons, their wives and children, and the important jobs each of them had. "You must be very proud of them," Marv Trompkin said.

"Oh, I am," said Mrs. Arnsted. She paused briefly. "But you know," she said, "sometimes I wish they had never gone off to university. Then they would have had to stay on the farm and wouldn't be so far from home."

Sometimes stories told about tragic events. I remember the day I heard Ma Henderson tell about the death of one of her daughters. I don't know what Ma's real name was, but even when she was a young woman everyone in town called her Ma—even people a lot older than she was.

I was ten or twelve years old when I heard her tell the story. We were in a car going between Deer River and New Cambridge. The road there follows the railroad tracks, and there are mile signs along the railroad that go from about mile seventy-five at New Cambridge to mile ninety-eight at Deer River. As we passed mile post number seventy-nine, Ma Henderson said to the adults in the car that she never could go past that sign without thinking of her daughter Teresa, who had died from a ruptured appendix thirty-five years earlier.

"There was a terrible blizzard that night," she said, "and Teresa had already been sick for two days. Doc Sawyer was here then, but he was in the hospital himself for that gallbladder operation he had, so we didn't really know what to do. During the blizzard Teresa got sicker. She had terrible stomach pains so we decided that blizzard or no blizzard we would get her to a hospital. We didn't have a car yet, but there were already quite a few around at that time, so we got Mac Smith, who used to work for the railroad, to take us.

"The closest hospital back then was in Chandlier, which was over an hour away in good weather, but Mac had a big car and we thought we could get through the snow all right. He picked us up about eight-thirty at night. My husband rode in the front seat beside Mac, and I rode in the back seat holding Teresa. The snow seemed to let up as we drove, but the car still couldn't go full speed because the drifts were so deep.

"My little girl didn't have a chance really. We didn't find out until later that it was her appendix. She started to cry somewhere between home and New Cambridge, and she died in my arms at mile seventy-nine. When she stopped crying I looked up, and through the falling snow I could see that sign. And I never go by it now without thinking of that night."

And whenever I go back to Deer River now, and go past that sign on the way to New Cambridge, I remember Ma Henderson's story.

Mostly
Hunting Stories

To a certain extent at least, the changing seasons brought a change in the kind of stories that were told in Deer River. In the winter, tales of cold weather and snow storms were told and re-told. In the spring and summer the stories were more apt to be about farming or fishing. In the autumn, though, more than at any other time of the year, people talked about their hunting exploits.

Most of these stories were about the location and methods of individual hunts. They were tales about shooting a particular six-point buck, or a day when somebody got his limit of upland game birds, or perhaps how an excellent chance to shoot a moose was missed. Sometimes a hunting story took on wider dimensions, however.

"I'll tell you about the smartest hunter I've ever heard about," Pete Hawkins said one fall afternoon. "He lived here in Deer River back when people first homesteaded this area. I couldn't tell you his name now, but my father used to tell me the story and he knew the name then.

"Back in them days people didn't have the money they do now, and one winter this fellow went out to try to shoot a deer. He only had one shell left for his rifle and his family needed the meat, so he knew that he'd have to make his shot count.

"He hunted around for a while and finally came upon a nice young buck. There was a lot more game in the area in those days. He raised his gun to shoot, but just then he noticed a cougar between him and the deer. Now, this fellow didn't know what to do. He didn't want to shoot the deer and be left near a cougar with no way to protect himself. On the other hand, he didn't want to shoot the cougar because then he wouldn't be able to get the deer for meat for his family.

"He was downwind from both animals so he just stayed put and before long he saw that the cougar was hunting deer too. Well, when he figured that out, this homesteader knew what he should do. He just waited until the cougar jumped the deer and killed it. Then he shot the cougar and took both animals home."

One fall day Charlie Maystead told a hunting story.

"When I was a kid," he said, "I used to go hunting with my uncle quite a lot. He didn't have children of his own so he enjoyed taking me. We'd go all over the area to hunt. Every year he took me deer hunting too, and one year we went up north to hunt elk.

"Now, Uncle John was always playing around trying to scare me. Of course, I'd never let on that anything he ever did bothered me, and sometimes I'd do things to try and startle him, just to get even. I'd come up and poke him in the ribs when he wasn't looking, or something. If he could help it he wouldn't let on like he even noticed anything I did.

"One day he took me grouse hunting over between the farm where I grew up and the north sandhills. We walked some fields over there for a couple of hours, but we didn't have a dog with us and so we didn't scare up anything.

"On the way back to the car Uncle John was in the lead. I was a dozen steps or so behind him and all of a sudden my gun went off. It was that little twenty gauge that I've still got at home. I must have touched the trigger without realizing it. I don't have a clue why the safety wasn't on, but I can still hear the boom that shotgun made in my head. I swear it's the loudest noise I've ever heard.

"The barrel was pointed down and a bit in front of me, and I came close to shooting my Uncle John in the back of his legs. The shot hit just behind him and scattered gravel across the ground like stones across water. I think some even hit the back of Uncle John's boots.

"He never turned around, though; he just kept walking and never said a word. I was shaking so bad I could hardly keep hold of the twenty gauge. By the time we got back to the car I'd calmed down enough to hide my shakes. Uncle John still hadn't said anything. As we were driving away, though, he asked if I hadn't shot kind of close. 'Naw,' I said, 'I missed you by ten feet anyway.' Uncle John never mentioned another thing about it. See, he figured that I was just trying to scare him and he didn't want to let on that I'd worried him any."

When Sparky Anderson heard Charlie tell his story he thought of a similar tale.

"That reminds me of a story Tom Hannah told me about Walter Higgons and Duke Dupuis," Sparky said. "Now those two old men won't so much as speak to each other today. They haven't for twenty-five years or more, but at one time they were neighbors and evidently very good friends. I think they even went to school together, and they used to hunt and fish together all the time.

"Anyway, Tom told me that old Duke was always playin' jokes on Walter; always tryin' to scare him the way Charlie's Uncle John did Charlie. One time Duke and Walter were huntin' up near Casper's Creek and Walter got an idea to get even.

"He was walkin' a yard or so behind Duke. They were tryin' to scare up some grouse I suppose. Anyway, Walter took his shotgun in his left hand, pointed it up and behind him, and pulled the trigger. At the same time he cuffed Duke behind the head as hard as he could with his other hand. Duke fell on the ground screaming that he'd been shot before the shotgun had finished roaring.

" 'You've shot me,' he kept cryin' over and over. 'You've shot me, Walter.' Walter, in the meanwhile, had fell to the ground himself because he was laughin' so hard. Duke kept hollerin', 'You've shot me!' and slappin' his hand across the back of his head lookin' for blood.

"Of course, he never found any, and after a while it came to him that it wasn't right for Walter to be lyin' there laughin' if he had just shot somebody. I don't know where Tom heard the story, but he said that when Duke figured out that Walter had made a fool of him he chased him down and beat him half to death, bloodied his nose and mouth anyway. And that, according to Tom Hannah, is how Walter and Duke stopped bein' friends."

At this point the topic of conversation changed from hunting tales to Walter and Duke. Jake Peters said that he had heard that their long-time feud had started a different way.

"It was back in prohibition time," Jake said, "way before I came out to this country, but it was just like it was back home. You could still get a drink of whiskey if you wanted one. The only thing different then than now is that now it is legal and then it was cheaper. Heimi Bontrigger had a poolroom back then and you could go there and get a drink any time you wanted one. Heimi sold whiskey right from the barrel.

"One day Walter and Duke were in there having a snip or two, and all of a sudden Walter says, 'Heimi, this whiskey tastes like it's got iron in it.' Well, Heimi and a couple of other guys tasted it—you had to be careful about getting bad liquor back then—but nobody but Walter could taste the iron.

"Duke kept sipping at the whiskey, though, and after a while he says, 'Walter, that whiskey don't taste like iron, it tastes like shoe leather.' Well, nobody else could taste any leather in it either, but Walter and Duke were both sure as the devil that the whiskey had a taste to it. Before long they were arguing over whether it tasted like iron or leather. They kept tasting it, and the more they tasted the more they were convinced that the other fellow was wrong.

"After a while they were both pretty drunk from all the tasting, and one or the other of them hit the other one. The story I got was that Duke gave Walter a beating out in the alley behind the poolroom, and Heimi wouldn't let either one of them in again until after prohibition was over.

"The really amazing thing about the whole episode," Jake said, "was that when the whiskey barrel was empty, Heimi opened it up and found a piece of leather about the size of a dime attached to the inside of the barrel with an iron nail."

After Jake's story Pete Hawkins told about when old Duke thought he was going to die. Everyone had heard the story before, but as Sparky always said, "People don't think there's anything wrong when someone sings a song they've already heard, so they don't need to complain when they hear a story a second time."

"That time old Duke ate the bad meat I guess it gave him such terrible pains he thought he was going to die," Pete said. "He was about eighty then and along in the night sometime he sent word to get Walter Higgons to come.

"Now, I wasn't there, of course, but the way I understand it is that when Walter got there Duke was full of remorse and asked Walter to forgive him for all the bad things he'd ever said about him. I guess it was a pretty emotional meeting, the two old enemies making up and forgiving each other.

"Then the next day, of course, Duke got better. The day after that he saw Walter on the street. 'Damn you, Walter,' he said. 'I wasn't as sick as I thought I was so I'm taking back all them things I told you the other night.'

"Now, of course, Duke and Walter don't speak to each other again."

After that story the talk returned to hunting. Sparky Anderson told a tale about the time he shot two snow geese with one shot. Jake Peters told about shooting an albino mallard. Charlie Maystead told about seeing an albino elk one time in the sand-hills.

Then Sparky Anderson told the story of the best day's hunt he had ever had. It was in the sandhills, and he shot an elk, got his limit of grouse, and then shot a Canada goose, all in the same day. Pete Hawkins said that that was a fair day's hunt all right, but he thought he could go one better.

"The best day I ever had," Pete said, "I was hunting with an old muzzle loader that Harv Arnsted had reconditioned. Harv had been after me to try it out for some time. He had that job with the government then, and one night I saw him in town here and told him that I was thinking about going hunting in the morning and would give his muzzle loader a try if he still was offering it.

"It was deer season and I thought the idea of a muzzle loader seemed kind of sporting. Harv thought it was a good idea too, and told me to come by the house the next morning and get it. He said he'd give me some lessons with it before I left.

"The next morning when I got there, though, Harv had already left. Mary said that when he'd talked to me he'd forgotten that he had to be in New Cambridge early in the morning. He had left the rifle for me to use, though, along with a horn of powder and some lead bullets.

"I thanked Mary, took the gun, and then drove out to a spot I knew by Swan Creek, just past where the road cuts off to go to Sparta. It was a beautiful morning when I got there. I put a double load of powder in the gun, tapped it down real nice, and then put in the lead. I was ready to hunt. What I didn't know was that Mary had forgotten to tell me that Harv had already tapped in a double load of powder. At least that's what Harv told me happened when I talked to him later. Maybe he just forgot to tell Mary.

"Anyway, I pulled on a pair of hip boots and went down to the creek. I thought I'd wade across to the other side and wait by an old cottonwood tree there by the river. It was just starting to get light by this time, and I had a feeling it was going to be a good morning to be hunting.

"Then, just as I got to the edge of the creek, I noticed a mallard duck just over the bank. And then I flushed half a dozen sharp-tailed grouse from the grass, and they flew up onto a branch of an old bur oak tree. I was kind of watching those grouse when I noticed a black bear coming up the riverbank on the other side of the tree.

"Well, I raised the rifle to shoot the bear, but just then a big eight-point buck came walking out of the trees just to the right of where the bear was. I stopped to look at the deer, and then I noticed a rabbit on the bank across the creek.

"I figured I couldn't get both the bear and the deer with that old muzzle loader, so I raised the gun to shoot the bear when all of a sudden he raised up on his hind legs and looked right at me. It was like watching a wildlife film on television, only it kind of scared me and I jerked the gun a little high as I shot.

"Now, when those four loads of powder went off, that gun more or less exploded. The barrel split right in two. One part hit the deer and killed it. The other half killed the bear. My shot was high and the bullet split the limb those grouse were perched on, right down its center halfway to the tree. There was enough tension in that old oak, though, that after the bullet passed through the limb it snapped back together, catching each one of those grouse by their feet.

"The bullet went on past the tree, hit a rock, and ricocheted across the river and killed the rabbit. The force of the explosion knocked me backwards and I fell into the river right on top of the duck. I don't know how I had the presence of mind to grab it, but I did.

"So there I was. With one shot I had killed an eight-point buck, a black bear, and a rabbit. Besides that I'd captured six sharp-tailed grouse and a mallard duck alive.... But do you know, boys, the most amazing thing about that little incident was that when I came up out of the river my boots were full of trout."

Milt
Moyer

Milt Moyer was short and fat and usually talkative. For forty years Milt ran the post office in Deer River, and during most of those years the building's lobby served as one of the town's favorite spots for swapping tales. Originally the post office had been in Arnold Bascum's father's general store, and Milt began his career as a postman by becoming a clerk there.

Soon after he started in the grocery business, however, the government centralized the postal service for the area, and the Deer River office, because the town was along the railroad, became the sole post office in an area that had once had half a dozen. Rather than run the new post office, the Bascums decided to stay in business for themselves and keep their general store. The post office moved to a wood-frame building across the street and Milt became the new postmaster.

By the mid-1950s, when Milt began to think about retiring, the post office was the second oldest building along Deer River's main street. The clean white outside walls always seemed freshly painted, but on the inside of the building its age was more apparent. The lobby was divided from the work area by an L-shaped wall of postal lock boxes and a yellowed pine counter that extended across half the width of the building. The wood floors were pocked with wear, and a visible path had been worn from the doorway to the counter. A long wooden bench was under the big window at the front of the building, and sometimes half a dozen people would sit on it talking with Milt and his customers, who would stand in the lobby to visit if the bench was full.

The talk in the post office was about the same as it was other places in Deer River; it was about the weather, or crops, or hunting, or how the family was doing, or the price of cattle, or maybe a series of funny stories or tall tales. One day, though, Pete and Sparky were teasing Milt about his upcoming retirement when Milt started talking about life in a small-town post office.

"Come on, Milt," Sparky said, "aren't you going to miss sittin' around the post office listenin' to us tell tales?"

"I can listen to those stories from that side of the counter just fine," said Milt.

"Yea, but you won't be getting paid for sitting around listening to Sparky's lies then," said Pete.

Milt didn't answer right away. He kind of stared off through the post office's front window at Deer River's main street. "You know, boys," he said, "you probably never thought much about it, but running a post office in a small town is a lot different than it would be in a city. I've got to know the people here, and try to get along with them. I mean in a city all a postmaster has to do is deliver mail as it's addressed, but in a small town it doesn't work that way.

"Take this morning. I got a letter addressed to P. Hawkins, Deer River. Now, Pete, that letter could have been for you, but there are three P. Hawkinses in Deer River, and I had to guess which one of you it was for. As it happened I knew this letter went to Paul Hawkins because it was from the Dairy Association, and he's the only Hawkins that belongs to it. But, you see, a city postmaster wouldn't have to know anything like that.

"Now, with you or Paul or Patrick it wouldn't make a lot of difference if I got one of your letters mixed up. You wouldn't complain a lot. But what about Harvey Miller—there are two Harvey Millers that get mail here you know, and they're not even related. And think about all the Arnsteds, and McKenzies, and

Hoppingarners, and Smiths, and Andersons that live around here. I have to keep them all straight. Do you know that if you count Joe, Jr. there are five Joe Arnsteds that live in the Deer River postal district, and three of them live on Town Line Road. . . .

"And another thing. Being a postmaster in a small town, about half the people accuse me of reading their mail, and the other half expect me to. I'll hand someone a letter and they'll say, 'Who is this from?' or I'll give them a package and they'll say, 'What is it?'

"Sometimes people will read their letter here in the lobby and talk to me about its contents as if I had already read it and knew who it was from and what it was about. And if it happens to be from a son or daughter who lives somewhere else, I'm sure to get the inside story about all the problems they're having, or what a bum they've married—and then, after they warn me not to tell a soul about things I never wanted to hear in the first place, they go next door to Bert's and tell everybody who they can get to listen the same story. . . .

"Do you know, I've worked in this post office for forty-two years and I don't think there have been more than half a dozen times that I've given someone a mail-order catalog that they haven't said, 'Oh, a wish book, eh?' I say it to myself now every time I pick up a catalog off the shelf to give to someone. 'A wish book, eh?' It comes as sure as the sun comes up in the morning. . . .

"And the money-order business. In a city you just sell the customer what he wants and have him fill it out, but in Deer River whenever people buy a money order they tell me what it's for: to pay a bill, buy some new clothes, alimony. Whatever it is, they tell me about it, and they don't spare the details.

"You really have to know your customers out here too, because sometimes it's just easier to fill out the money-order form yourself than get involved in their discussions about what's wrong with the world. They'll chat on and on as if I have nothing to do in here but pass the time. Meanwhile, of course, they'll have two or three kids that are tearing up the lobby or licking the decals off the front door. . . .

"Another thing—whenever people get a letter from the government they want me to explain it to them. It could be from the Department of Agriculture, or Veterans Affairs, or about taxes, but somehow it's my job to represent the government. What am I supposed to do? I don't know anything about taxes. . . ."

Milt paused and thought some more about his job in a small-town post office. "Of course, there's advantages to a small-town office too," he said. "When you get right down to it, I like knowing my customers. I like listening to people I know talk together here in the lobby, and I know every kid in town. Besides, I'll bet no city postmaster has customers who bring him fresh caught fish, or homemade bread and cookies. I'm looking forward to retirement, but you're right, I'm going to miss this place too."

"You know," Pete said, "I remember when I was a kid and the post office was still in the store. There would always be a bunch of old men sitting around the stove talking."

"That's right," said Milt. "Now we're the old men."

All Them Politicians Are . . .

Local elections in Deer River were fought on an almost invisible battlefield. An outsider could come to town before a vote and never suspect that an election was to take place. No campaign signs or automobile bumper stickers ever announced a voter's preferences. No local candidate ever made a speech or spent any money outside the beer parlor trying to get elected. It would have been considered poor taste.

This is not to say that there were never any political divisions in the town. It's just that political bickering and individual ambitions were usually controlled by the knowledge that opposing candidates and factions would still be neighbors long after the election was over. Occasionally, though, local politics would disrupt the normally calm waters of personal relationships in Deer River.

Jake Peters came into Bert's one day about two weeks before an election for the town councilors. He was laughing at a story he had just heard about Cal Murphey and Clayton Powell. They lived right across from each other on Third Street. Clayton was running in the election. So was Cal Murphey's brother-in-law Harvey Arnsted.

90

"Evidently," Jake said, "Cal had been sitting on his front porch in the swing when Clayton came out and sat on his front steps. I don't know how they got started, but before long they were yelling back and forth talking about the weather and what-have-you. I guess they often do that sort of thing. People up and down the road can hear them.

"Before long, though, they got to talking about the election, and everybody could tell they were getting mad at each other. Cal said that the town council was wasting money, and besides, it never did anything that amounted to a pinch of snuff. That made Clayton mad as a hungry hound dog. He told Cal that he didn't know what he was talking about, and then he said, 'Now listen here, Cal. I understand you've been telling people I'm a liar.' "

" 'I never did,' Cal yelled back. 'They must have found it out on their own.' "

One reason local elections created very little fanfare in Deer River was that by and large the ambitions of local candidates were not as suspect as those of seekers of higher offices. Those candidates were always looked at with a measure of suspicion. Sparky Anderson had a story about one such fellow who came to Deer River.

"This guy come to town campaignin' for somethin'," Sparky said, "and he gave a speech. After he was finished he went around shakin' hands, askin' people for their support. I don't even remember what he was runnin' for, but he shook hands with Oscar Hoppingarner and asked Oscar how he thought he would do against the candidate of the other party.

" 'That depends,' said Oscar, 'on which one of you sees the most people.'

" 'Oh,' said the candidate. 'You think I should get out and see as many voters as possible.'

" 'Well, that's up to you,' said Oscar. 'But the way I figure it, if you meet the most people, then he'll probably win; but if he meets the most people then I think you've got a pretty good chance.' "

Pete Hawkins had an election story too.

"One time another federal politican came to Deer River," Pete said. "It wasn't the same one Oscar talked too. This guy was the son of a prominent Anglican bishop. He made a little speech down at the post office, and afterwards some people from the

Anglican church in Farmington took him around to visit all the Anglicans in town.

"Evidently, one of the stops was at old Marv Watkins's house. You know how hard of hearing Marvin is. He missed most of what people were saying to him, but he figured out that the young man with them was running for office. People kept shouting to Marv that the gentleman was the son of a bishop, but Marv couldn't hear what they were saying.

"Finally, just before they were going to leave, one woman shouted into Marv's ear, 'He's the son of a bishop.'

"Marv looked startled for a minute and then said, 'Oh well, all them politicians are.' "

Sparky Anderson told a story about a woman he had heard about who lived in another part of the country. This woman raised chickens. She had a contract for eggs from some big company, but it always riled her how little she got for her eggs and how expensive they seemed to be in the stores. She figured the company must be getting all the profit, so one day she wrote a little note on the bottom of one of the eggs explaining that she was the farmer who raised the egg, and asking whoever bought it to write to her and let her know where they got it and how much they paid for it.

"Well, this lady didn't get any reply from her note for about two months," Sparky said. "Then she got an official-lookin' letter from the government. It was from the minister of agriculture. He said that he had received her egg for free while giving a speech in Ottawa."

Tom Hannah told a story about politics.

"My Uncle Clyde," he said, "hated all politicians. He said you couldn't trust any of them, especially if they were in the federal government. He said it was never any use to vote because even if you could find somebody that seemed honest enough to make it worth your bother, why he'd just do somethin' as soon as he got in that would make you ashamed you ever voted for him.

"Uncle Clyde only ever voted once," Tom said. "See, the way that happened was that he had a pretty good Jersey cow that got sick with the bloat. Now, my Uncle Clyde was as tightfisted as any man who ever walked the earth, but this was a pretty good cow so he called in a vet.

"The vet made the cow swallow some medicine, and then he tried to sell Uncle Clyde a fancy contraption to give the animal an enema with. That didn't set right with Uncle Clyde. He figured he could find somethin' around the house that would do the job just as well. The vet admitted that most anything would work, so my uncle bought the medicinal ingredients and the vet went home.

"Uncle Clyde searched all over the farm for somethin' to administer the dosage in, but he couldn't find a thing. Finally, though, he came across an old moose call way up in the attic, and he took it down to the barn. He stuck the small end in the appropriate place and poured the medicine the vet had sold him down the spout. Pretty soon that stuff got to bubblin' and workin' around in there like store-bought drain cleaner in a plugged sink.

"When the liquid worked its way through, though, all that pressure that had been buildin' up inside that cow was free. Liquid commenced shootin' out of that moose call sprayin' all over the inside of the barn, and after the water was gone there was still more air. That old moose call began to sing.

"Now, as luck would have it, there was a bull moose passin' somewhere nearby, because as soon as that moose call went off he busted through the back of the barn after that cow.

"Uncle Clyde's cow, of course, didn't want any part of a bull moose, so she headed out the front door of the barn as quick as the moose came in the back. The whole thing must have been some sight because once free, that cow just kept right on runnin' and that moose call just kept right on tootin'. And the moose just followed them down the road tryin' to catch up.

"About a half mile down from Uncle Clyde's there was a government drawbridge over the Swan River, and when the man who ran it heard the moose call he thought there was a steamboat comin' so he raised the bridge. Uncle Clyde's cow ran right off the end and fell in the river and drowned. . . .

"About a year later the fellow that took care of the drawbridge ran for a position on the school board, and Uncle Clyde voted for the first time in his life. He said that any man who didn't know the difference between a steamboat and a cow with a moose call up her arse shouldn't have anything to do with educating children."

Gossip
and More

Men and women in Deer River were equally inclined towards gossip, but there were differences in the things they gossiped about. Women generally opted for the gossip of petty scandal, while the men talked about other people's mistakes.

For example, one day in Bert's, Sparky Anderson asked Pete Hawkins if he happened to notice the way the boy Mac Harriman had hired had stacked his bale wagon. "It's a wonder it didn't fall over before he got it out of the field," Sparky said.

"That's not as bad as Marv Arnsted's new hand," Jake Peters said. "Oscar Hoppingarner told me he drove Marv's Allis Chalmers into the barn and forgot to duck his head going through the door. It knocked him off the tractor and the manure wagon ran over him. Worst thing was that the Allis kept going and put a hole through the back of the barn."

"Yea, and it probably took old Marv about a week to discover the hole," said Jim McKenzie.

At the same time this discussion was taking place at Bert's, Jim's wife Donna was at their home telling Daphne Hagalgance how Mabel Price only brought one cake to the sewing club bake sale the week before. "Everybody else brought at least three or four items," Donna said, "but Mabel just brought this little nine-inch cake with a really thin layer of vanilla icing on it so the chocolate cake showed through."

Donna said that the worst part was that when nobody bought the cake Mabel took it home with her. . . .

Men and women in Deer River also told different kinds of stories. Men's stories were more apt to be about people you knew, and they were most often meant to make you laugh. Women's stories could be funny too, especially when they talked about their children, but just as often the stories women told were more ominous. They created tales of ill-health and almost bizarre tragedies. As often as not they were about people we didn't know, or knew only through someone else.

"Did you hear what happened to Betty Hoppingarner's cousin?" Kate Arnsted asked Phyllis Smith one day after they ran into each other at Josh Peterson's hardware store. "I think her name is Wilma something-or-other. She lives up at Franklin, but she's been here in Deer River before. I think she and her husband came to a hockey tournament here a couple of years ago.

"Anyway, this Wilma was in the doctor's office up at Franklin and she got to talking with another woman there. This woman and her husband have a dairy farm, and last spring she helped pull a calf that was born dead. The strange thing, though, was that this calf didn't have any front feet. The woman told her husband that it was a sign of some kind, but he just laughed at her. Two weeks later, though, he got caught in an auger and they had to amputate both of his hands."

When women told humorous stories they were often about their children.

Lily Hawkins liked to tell about her daughter Denise who, when she was about four, went with the family to visit some cousins who had a farm in the east. "They didn't have inside plumbing yet," Lily said, "and the first time Denise had to use the washroom I took her and showed her where it was and then went back to the house.

"After a while I noticed that she hadn't come back so I started watching for her out the kitchen window. I could see the door to the outhouse was still closed and latched from the inside. After about twenty minutes I walked down the path. I could hear

Denise crying before I got there, and so I thought maybe she was having trouble going, so I went in and told her not to worry, to just come back to the house, that it was all right.

"Denise looked up at me and whimpered, 'But mommy, where do you flush it?' "

Beatrice Adams told about the time her three-year-old daughter Carolyn wanted to take a walk by herself. "First she wanted to walk out to the farm and visit her grandmother, which is about two miles. I told her no to that one. Then she wanted to walk around the block by herself. I still thought she was too young to walk so far, but she kept asking me to go. And then her brother Mark, who was just five then, volunteered to go along and watch her.

"Well, Carolyn had never been anywhere without me, so I decided to let her go. But I made Mark promise to watch her carefully.

"Now, even a slow walk around the block shouldn't take over ten minutes—even for a three- and a five-year-old. I waited for about five minutes and then started walking around the block in the opposite direction so I would meet them. I didn't see a sign of them until I was three-quarters of the way back home and found the five-year-old kicking a stone along the sidewalk, apparently carefree, with Carolyn nowhere to be seen.

" 'Mark,' I said, 'where's your little sister?'

"He looked up at me, smiled proudly and said, 'Mom, it's a good thing you told me to watch her 'cause she's gone to Gramma's. . . .'

"Carolyn was a good half-mile from home when I caught up to her, and mad at me when I made her come home. . . . And her, not a month past her third birthday."

Instead of stories about children, sometimes the tales women told were about giving birth to them.

One day Cynthia Anderson, Lorna Currier, and Joan Peters were talking about the length and difficulties of their respective labors. Cynthia told about a cousin of hers who gave birth to a healthy eight-pound baby boy on the stretcher on the way to the delivery room.

"Oh yes, for some women having a baby is very fast," said Lorna Currier. "My sister Louise was only in labor for two hours before her first baby, and then only forty-five minutes for baby number two. Both babies were early and when she got pregnant a third time the doctor told her to come to the hospital even if she felt like she was going to cut wind. . . .

"But do you know, when the third baby finally came, she was in labor for two days."

Morley Can't Shoot Straight

Morley Parker and his wife Sarah lived about halfway between Deer River and Sparta. If anybody around Deer River fit the image of an old codger it was Morley. He always wore a week's worth of grizzled beard and an old grease-stained cap that had the emblem of the New York Yankees above the brim. Morley and Sarah ran a diversified farm that included goats, pigs, two milk cows, and some chickens. The couple and their farm were common fuel for stories around Deer River. Although most of the tales were untrue, some of them were at least partly based on fact.

One morning Sparky Anderson came into Bert's chuckling to himself and telling everyone he had a new story about Morley.

"I stopped over to the Parkers' farm this mornin' to buy a dozen eggs," Sparky said, "and Mrs. Parker told me she didn't have any to sell. She said all but two of their chickens were dead. Well, I'd just been by there the week before and they'd had about forty-five layin' hens. Morley had told me then that they'd been havin' some trouble with a skunk or a weasel or some varmint gettin' in after 'em, so I asked Mrs. Parker if they had caught whatever it was that was killin' so many.

"She kinda smiled a little sheepishly, and then she told me the story. They had put out some traps and had been leaving the shotgun by the back door for a week with no good results, she said. Then, the night before last, they heard a noise comin' from the chicken house. Well, Morley got up in a hurry and headed for the clucker coop. He didn't even take the time to get dressed; he just slipped on his boots, grabbed the gun and flashlight that were waiting by the back door, and ran outside to the chicken house with nothing on but his long-legged underwear—you know, the kind with the trap door in the back.

"Morley snuck into the chicken house sighting his power-beam flashlight and that big twelve gauge shotgun of his along the chicken roost. Just then William, that long-jawed coon hound of Morley's, come up and cold-nosed where the trap door was hangin' open. Morley raised up a might surprised, the shotgun went off . . . and he and Mrs. Parker spent the rest of the night cleanin' chickens."

The great thing about Sparky's new story about Morley was that everyone there already knew a similar tale about him that had taken place thirty years before. After Sparky finished his tale nobody said anything for a while, but everyone was thinking about the old story. Finally Jake Peters volunteered to re-tell it.

"You know," Jake said, "that story reminds me of the time Morley and his father were hunting moose up by the national park. Morley was only about twenty-five or thirty years old then. It was ten or fifteen years before his father passed away.

"See, the two of them went up in the hills along the national park border hoping to get an animal that had maybe strayed outside the boundaries. They walked in a couple of miles from the highway and they took an old horse with them so they wouldn't have to pack any moose meat out on their backs.

"When they got in far enough, Morley tied the horse to a tree and they walked along a ridge right at the park border. Then Morley cut down through some lower ground to the south while his dad continued along the ridge hoping to run an animal out past where Morley would be waiting.

"I never did learn for sure if the horse got loose or if Morley got turned around in his directions, but somehow he came up on his horse again and shot it by mistake. Even after the horse hit the ground Morley didn't realize what he had done. His dad called to him when he heard the shot, and Morley answered that he'd killed a moose, but it was a young one.

"Old Mr. Parker used to tell the story around town that when he got over to where the horse was lying, Morley was just standing there shaking his head. He'd just figured out what he'd done, and he looked up at his dad and said, 'A young moose and an old horse don't look much alike do they?' "

One of the joys of storytelling is that when it's going well, one story will lead to another. The subject matter rarely stays on a single topic, however. A small part of one tale will remind someone of a story about something entirely different, and a small part of the new yarn will remind someone else of another story about an entirely new subject.

When Jake finished the story about Morley shooting his own horse, Pete Hawkins said, "You know, hearing that story about Morley shooting moose up on the park boundary reminds me of the time Walter Maxwell and his brother Perry got caught poaching moose up in the park.

"It was right at that time when the prime minister and half the cabinet were out in this part of the country giving a bunch of speeches. They'd been up in Hastings for some kind of a big do, and they were going to be in Austin for another one the next day.

"Walter, of course, didn't pay any attention to the political goings on. He wouldn't have cared a lick if all them folks would have come right here to Deer River, so it certainly didn't matter to him that they were a hundred miles away in Hastings. He and Perry were in the park spotlighting that night, just like always. As you know, those boys are apt to do those sorts of things.

"This particular night they should have been home listening to the news, though, because those politicians were planning to go right down Route 5 through the park to Austin, and they had a whole caravan of Mounties escorting them.

"Walter and Perry, though, didn't know anything about it. They went into the park, shot their moose, and were parked right on the highway trying to load the animal into the pickup when that caravan of police officers came over the hill.

"Perry told me later there were about ten carloads of them,

and every car had its lights flashing. He said that when the first car came into sight he and Walter ran into the bush, but when they looked back and saw all those Mounties they just walked out onto the highway with their hands up, thinking it was no use to try to outrun the whole detachment. He said that they rode in the car behind the prime minister's all the way to Austin . . . but never did get a chance to shake his hand."

After Pete's story Jake Peters told another one.

"That reminds me," he said, "of a story old Mr. Trompkin told me once about Walter and Perry's father. His name was Albert Maxwell, I think, but I don't remember him myself. Mr. Trompkin said Albert and his wife used to fight something fierce whenever they came to town.

"Evidently, old Mrs. Maxwell was very domineering, and if Albert didn't do things her way there was hell to pay when they got home. And sometimes she didn't wait until they got home. Mr. Trompkin said he'd seen her take a buggy whip to Albert a couple of times out on Main Street, and one time she threw a can of beans at him right in the store.

"Another time Mr. and Mrs. Maxwell had a fight out on the street and everybody in town stopped what they were doing and listened to it. Afterwards, Albert came into the store to get some things and Mr. Trompkin asked why in the dickens he didn't just leave his wife at home when he came to town.

" 'Well,' Albert said, 'I figure it's easier to take her along than kiss her good-bye.' "

Farmin'

In any small town there are bound to be a lot of stories about farming. Deer River was no exception. Often the tales were about the poor prices for grain, or cattle, or other farm products. Sometimes, too, the talk would be about how expensive it was to farm.

Even back when I was growing up people talked about the high cost of seed, fuel, and tractor parts. I remember one time listening to Pete Hawkins telling about a second-hand tractor he had just bought. It was a small Ford and Pete said that he had bought one like it brand new shortly after the war. . . .

"I only kept that tractor a couple of years," Pete said, "and then I sold it to Clay Weatherburn up at Sparta for just a couple of hundred dollars less than I paid for it, so I thought I made out pretty good on the deal.

"Anyway, this spring I decided I needed a little chore tractor, just something I could use in the yard and maybe rake with at haying time. I thought an old Ford like I used to have would be pretty good so I started looking around for one, but the prices were all too high. I finally located one that wasn't too steep up at the John Deere dealer's in New Cambridge. I kind of laughed when I bought it because I had bought that first Ford from the same dealer, new, ten years ago and the price then was nearly a hundred dollars less than I paid for this used one.

"The worst of it, though, was that I got the tractor home and found out it was the same one I used to own. The very same tractor. I bought my own tractor back for more money than I sold it for . . . and more than I paid for it originally. I'll tell you one thing, nobody is going to tell me the cost of farm machinery isn't getting out of hand."

Sometimes farm stories were about earlier times. Stories about farming with horses stirred the romance in any storyteller's blood. "You can say what you want about farmin' with tractors," Sparky Anderson said, "but there's somethin' about followin' a horse around a field that makes you feel more alive and closer to the land than you can ever feel sittin' on a big Massey-Harris."

"And you can talk all you want to about horses," said Jim McKenzie, "but there used to be a lot more work to farming in them days. Not to mention the fact that horses are always getting out and running off. We still had horses when I was growing up and I can remember lots of mornings chasing horses when we should have been doing something else."

"These days I spend more time fixin' machinery than I ever spent chasin' horses," said Sparky.

Pete Hawkins said that he got along well with horses. "But you know," he said, "I can remember the day my dad brought home our first car. He had taken a good team of horses and a wagon to town, and he traded them in on a new Ford. Dad had never driven an automobile before in his life, but he drove that car home. When he came through the front gate, though, he forgot what he was doing, yelled, 'Whoa,' and pulled back on the steering wheel so hard it came off in his hands."

"Do you know," Jake Peters said, "I've spent my fair share of days behind a horse, and for my money these old-timers worked a lot harder than anybody today. I can't help but think of a story I heard about Bill McCormick.

"He's retired now and lives in town, has for fifteen or twenty years, but he used to farm out by Tom Hannah's. Always worked hard. He raised grain, cattle, a bunch of kids, and milked a lot of cows. Used to get up every morning at four-thirty, winter and summer, seven days a week, and never thought about taking a vacation.

"Anyway, to make a long story short, I heard the other day he still sets his alarm for four-thirty in the morning. Hattie, his wife, told me he has ever since he moved off the farm—not because he likes to get up that early, but because of the pleasure it gives him to turn the damn thing off and roll over and go back to sleep for another three hours."

Pete Hawkins said that he could remember a story his father had told about Bill McCormick.

"I think Bill told my dad this story himself," Pete said. "See, the McCormicks had seventeen children just about a year apart in age. Maybe a little more age difference, but not much.

"One time there was a champion bull that somebody brought to the fair over in New Cambridge and Bill took the family to see it. When they got there, though, he found out that there was an admission charge of five or ten cents to see the animal. This was over and above the cost of getting into the fair in the first place.

"Well, with seventeen kids Bill didn't figure he could afford to see the bull. Since he had already promised the kids, though, he went around and found the owner to see if he couldn't get some kind of a discount.

"When Bill told the guy he had all those children the man let everyone in for free. He told Bill that if he had fathered seventeen kids he thought the bull ought to see him."

One afternoon Jake, Pete, and Sparky were sitting in Bert's card room talking about how much work it took to farm successfully. "That's why I left the farm as soon as I was old enough to get away," Jake said. "Farming's hard work, and I don't like hard work."

Pete said that hard work never killed anyone, but Sparky said he wasn't so sure. "Maybe hard work never killed anybody," he said, "but just the same, I sure never heard of anybody restin' himself to death." Jake said he could remember a story about an old farmer back in Manitoba who came pretty close.

"This was back when times were hard," said Jake, "and there was a fellow back home named Northrup Henny who was so lazy that his wife Hazel finally took the seven kids and up and left him to keep the young ones from starvin' to death. Old Northrup stayed on in the house with an old black dog after they left, but he didn't develop any more ambition. In fact, he got lazier and lazier until he wouldn't do any work at all. People said that he used to get up at four o'clock in the morning just so he'd have more time to lie around.

"Old Northrup didn't tend a garden so he didn't have any vegetables put away for the winter, and he didn't grow any grain so he couldn't make any flour for bread. When he ran out of food altogether it got so bad that the dog ran off and old Northrup started getting skinnier and skinnier.

"People from all around got together and decided that the best thing to do would be to bury old Northrup to keep him from starving to death. Everybody agreed that he was about dead anyway since all he ever did was sit on his front porch staring at the horizon.

"The next Sunday they went and got old Northrup, put him in a coffin, loaded him on a wagon, and started for the cemetery.

"About halfway there, though, they met a stranger traveling in a wagon going in the opposite direction. When the newcomer heard what the townfolk were about to do to a man who was still alive he went into a righteous oration.

" 'My goodness, brothers,' he said, 'today is the Sabbath. You can't bury a man who's still alive on the Sabbath. Where's your Christian mercy? Why, if this man needs food then give it to him. I've got twelve bushels of beans right here on this wagon and I'm prepared to give the man half of them.'

"Just then a voice was heard from the coffin. 'Mister,' Northrup strained, 'are those beans shelled yet?'

" 'Shelled?' asked the man. 'Why, no. No, they're not.'

"From the coffin came Northrup's disappointed voice: 'Drive on, driver,' it said, 'drive on.' "

Sometimes people in Deer River would get into rather heated arguments over topics like which company built the best tractor, the best time to plant fall rye, or when spring would come. One day Tom Hannah walked into Bert's when a discussion of similar nature was going on about the qualities of the various woods used for fence posts. He hadn't had time to get his hat off before Jake Peters asked him which post would last longer, one made from willow or one from cedar.

"Willow," Tom answered without hesitating. And as soon as the words were out of his mouth everyone in the cafe started to holler; the ones who liked willow because their favorite wood had been anointed, the ones who liked cedar because they thought their wood had been slandered unfairly.

"I'd just like to know how much longer you think willow is going to last," said Sparky Anderson.

Tom quickly appraised the situation. "Oh, about fifteen minutes," he told Sparky.

That Ain't the Truth, Is It?

Tall tales were always popular in Deer River. Sometimes it was hard to determine, though, which stories were true and which were fictionalized. Tales recounting real incidents were occasionally stretched to make better yarns out of them. Liberties with the truth like this were acceptable so long as the resulting story was good enough to warrant the lie. Besides, the tale usually remained close enough to the facts for listeners to deduce what actually happened.

Other times, though, the stories were so outrageous that even the most gullible of Deer River's citizenry knew they were told in jest.

Sparky Anderson told a lot of stories about horse trading that fit this description. One time Pete Hawkins and Sparky were at an auction over in New Cambridge and the auctioneer offered a medium-sized roan mare for sale. Pete said the horse looked like she had a lot of Arab in her. Sparky said that he had once owned a horse that looked just about like her.

"You know, the horse I had got sick one time," Sparky said, "and I don't know to this day what was wrong with him. I never did see a horse before or since afflicted like he was. All he'd do was stand there in his stall, not looking left nor right. Never lying down, either. After about a week of this I called old Doc Harvey and he come down to look at him.

"Doc examined him real good, took blood samples and ever' other kind of sample available and sent the whole works away to a lab at the veterinary college. In a couple of weeks he called back. 'The tests are inconclusive,' he said. 'Best thing to do is give him a quart of whiskey once a day for two weeks.'

"Well, I started that afternoon. But as soon as I tried to get the horse to swallow that whiskey he came to life, buckin' and kickin' and flingin' himself around the barn like a bobcat had him by the tail. I finally got a twitch over his nose and poured in the whiskey.

"When it was over I let the horse into the pasture and sat down and drank the other half myself I was so worn out. The next afternoon when I come to give him his medicine I had a little trouble catching him, but he didn't put up near so much fight drinkin' the stuff. I still drank a little myself afterwards, though, out of sympathy. After that I didn't have no more problems with that horse. I'd go out there at medicine time, and he'd be waitin' for me at the pasture gate. And do you know, when the time came to sell him I hated to see that horse go. We'd become pretty good drinkin' buddies."

Jake Peters told a lot of stories about working in lumber camps. One day after two or three true stories he talked about a cold winter day when an accident left one of his fellow workers decapitated.

"After the accident we stuck his head back on and packed snow around it to hold everything in place," said Jake. "It was about forty degrees below zero that day, and in about thirty seconds he seemed to get his breath back and was okay. We walked back to camp, but when we got into the bunkhouse the heat began to melt the snow and his head fell off again. It rolled across the floor and hit a jack-pine log by the fireplace. And do you know, the blow killed him."

Sparky Anderson said that Jake's story reminded him of something that happened to him when he was a kid.

"You know how people say cats have nine lives," he said. "Well, I know how that story got started. See, we had this old tomcat when I was a boy, and he got run over by a couple of horses. It didn't kill him, but he got banged up so bad that mom said the best thing would be to put him out of his misery. Since I was the oldest and dad wasn't home she told me to do the job.

"Well, I didn't like the idea much, but I saw that it had to be done. I put that cat in an old gunny sack we had, tied the end, and dropped the whole works into the creek that ran near our house.

"I hadn't been back inside for five minutes after I did it, though, than my mother yelled at me from the kitchen. 'Sparky,' she said, 'I thought you told me that you had killed that cat.' I told her I had, but when I looked out the window here came that tom walkin' up the lane. I reckon I didn't get the sack tied tight enough.

"Anyway, my mother sent me out with that cat again. This time I took along a little twenty gauge shotgun that I had when I was a kid. I put the cat down by an old log, aimed the gun, closed my eyes, and fired. Then I turned around and ran.

"When I got home I told my mother that I had killed the cat for sure that time, but in about five minutes she came in and said, 'Now, Sparky, that cat is back again.' I looked out the window and sure enough that cat was acomin' down the lane.

"The next time I knew I couldn't allow for any mistakes. I got the cat, took him out to the woodyard, and chopped off his head. I was so sick with what I had done that I just turned around and ran back to the house afterwards. . . . But five minutes later I looked out the window and here come that cat down the lane carryin' his head in his mouth."

Another time Sparky told a story about a fish he had caught once during a summer drought.

"It was so dry that year," Sparky said, "that the chickens were layin' powdered eggs. At my place that little creek that goes through my back quarter was dryin' up. I went out there one day and there was just little puddles of water along the creek bed, and in one puddle I found a pretty good-sized fish floppin' around. There wasn't much water, but that fish was still pretty alive so I picked him up and carried him home. I figured I could eat him for supper.

"When I got back to the yard, though, I had a couple of other things to do besides clean that fish, so I just tossed him in an old water bucket I had in the barn. Then I forgot about him until evenin'.

"By the time I remembered him that night, though, I didn't feel much like cleanin' him so I just tossed him out into the grass. The next mornin' I got up, and I'll be darn if that fish wasn't still alive. See, he'd kind of lived off the dew on the grass all night, I guess.

"I thought the whole thing was pretty remarkable so I went to workin' with that fish. I'd leave him in the bucket a few hours, then throw him out in the yard for a while, then back into the water for a spell. Every night, though, I'd just leave him in the yard, and he became quite domesticated. I started callin' him Raymond.

"Gradually, I just left Raymond out of the bucket longer and longer. I kept workin' with him and workin' with him until finally he didn't go near the water at all. Livin' on land was hard on him at first, though. I had to spray him for ticks a couple of times, and it took me half the summer to find something to feed him that he seemed to like.

"I tried all kinds of animal feeds, but he didn't seem to care for anything but chicken feed, so I just kept him in with the chickens after that. I fed him hen layer-diet and oyster shell just like the rest of them. After about a month on that feed Raymond started layin' an egg every second day. It always smelled a little fishy when you fried it, but other than that you couldn't tell Raymond's egg from the chickens'.

"I thought, by golly I've got something here, so I wrote a letter to the agricultural school and before long one of those professors came out here to see Raymond. I took him on out to the barnyard, but do you know I couldn't find that fish anywhere. We looked around for nearly half an hour before I finally found his body. The poor thing had climbed up on the cattle trough to get a drink of water, slipped on the ledge, and fell in the water and drowned."

Poor
Sparkies

Sparky Anderson had a special brand of story that Pete Hawkins called Poor Sparkies. These were tales that Sparky told on himself, and usually emphasized his tough luck, poverty, or foolishness.

"One time when I was about ten," Sparky told the assembled crowd in Bert's one day, "I went with my parents to visit a maiden aunt who lived in Austin. I didn't know it, but she had a cocker spaniel named Sparky. When we first got to Aunt Mary's house I went and played in the back yard while my parents visited.

"After a while, though, I got tired of being outside by myself, and went in the back door. Aunt Mary was in the kitchen cookin', and I started to take off my coat and boots. I was in the back room, but I could see into the kitchen easy enough. I didn't think Aunt Mary even knew I was there, but all at once she said, 'Sparky, you stink. Get on out of here.'

"Well, I was mortified. I was so ashamed I put my coat back on and went back outside and sat in the car. I must have been there about an hour before my dad came lookin' for me. He tried to get me to come in the house, but I wouldn't do it.

"Finally, he got me to tell him what was wrong, and after he thought about it awhile he figured out my aunt was talkin' to the dog. Then he took me inside and told the story to my mother and aunt, and everybody had a good laugh about it ... everybody except me, that is."

Sparky usually made his first stop at Bert's sometime before nine A.M. One day, though, he didn't arrive until nearly eleven.

"Where you been?" Bert called as Sparky came through the door.

"Had a busy morning," Sparky said. "I just come from the bank."

"What'd you do," Bert asked, "withdraw your life's savings?"

"Yup," said Sparky, "and the teller asked me how I wanted it, heads or tails."

Another time Sparky was at a livestock auction in New Cambridge, and he left his truck parked in the way of a trailer-load of hogs. When the driver came in the auction barn he asked Sparky and a group of men standing by the door if they knew who owned the blue Ford pickup parked by the gate.

"Well," said Sparky, "my bank owns it, but I drive it."

Sparky liked to tell about a time when he was about fourteen and courting his first girlfriend.

"I won't tell you who she was," Sparky always said, "because she lives right here in this town now. One day when we were kids and she was over to our place visitin', she embarrassed me so bad I still get red in the face when I see her.

"It was a bright summer day and we were sittin' on a rail fence that ran along one section of the cow pasture. Now, as we're asittin' there I couldn't help but notice that the bull was workin' that day, and I was sure she saw him too. The old devil was only about fifty yards from us ridin' a cow.

"Well, I didn't say anything at first, but the more I got to thinkin' about it, the more it seemed like an opportune time to bring our discussions around to sex. Finally, as I nodded my head towards the cow and bull, I said to her, 'Gee, you know, I wouldn't mind doin' some of that.'

"My girlfriend looked shocked. She turned to me like she was absolutely disgusted and said, 'Well, nobody's stoppin' you, and there's lots more cows.' "

After Sparky finished telling that story he'd as often as not go on to tell another tale that took place in the same pasture field.

"That field bordered the railroad tracks," he said, "and we had a bull once who was always breakin' out of the fence. He wasn't a mean animal really, but he was stubborn. We had just about got tired enough of fixin' fences and gates to sell him when one day I was on my way to get the cows and noticed the bull was gone again. He usually broke through the gate on the east end of the pasture, but this time he wasn't there.

"Then I heard the train whistle, looked up, and saw him on the railroad tracks. I tried to get to him but there wasn't enough time. The train was bearing down on him too fast. The last thing I ever saw of that bull was when he turned and faced the locomotive. He put his head down and shook it, then pawed the ground like he was going to charge. . . . I can't say he was a very smart bull, but he sure wasn't afraid of anything."

Sometimes Poor Sparkies turned out to be blow-by-blow accounts from Sparky's daily life. I remember one rainy day when Sparky came into Bascum's. Everybody was sitting around the stove, but no one was saying much.

Sparky sat down and after a short silence said, "You know, I don't know why I ever go anywhere near a city. Yesterday was kind of a poor day here for weather—kind of like today—and I needed to do some shoppin' for different things, so I decided I might just as well take a trip to Hastings. I don't know why I ever get such darn foolishness in my head, but it comes over me about ever' six months like a spell of some kind. I always regret it later. Anyway, like I said, yesterday I went up to Hastings.

"First, I needed a timing chain for that old truck of mine, so I stopped at an auto supply store. I took the old chain with me so I could show them what I needed, but the guy in the store looked at it in disbelief. 'Do you mean to tell me you've been drivin' somethin' that that chain came off of?' he asked. It was so messed up he couldn't believe that I took it off an engine that ran. I told him that when you were poor you had to make things last, so he went and found me a new one okay.

"When I asked him if he didn't have some instructions for putting the new one on he just looked at me and said, 'Oh, just throw it under the hood. With your luck that's all you'll need.' "

"After I left the auto parts store," Sparky said, "I drove clear across town to get some parts for that Allis Chalmers of mine. When I got there, though, they didn't have what I needed. I said, 'Gee, I thought you folks were supposed to keep tractor parts here,' and the guy says, 'We do, but not for anything that old.' I said, 'Oh, I guess you only keep spare parts for new tractors.' The fellow couldn't see the humor in that so I went on with my errands.

"I went to three or four other places, and had just about as much luck ever' place I went. At the end of the day I stopped at a little cafe to get a hamburger. When I came outside again there was a little terrier dog about the size of a rabbit that was tied by its leash to a lamppost. The little fella had got his leash all tangled around the post so that he only had an inch and a half or so of rope left.

"Well, it looked like a nice enough little dog, and I felt sorry for it, so I stopped and untangled the poor critter from the post. As soon as he was free, though, he turned vicious and jumped on me. The damn thing bit me about three times before I could get him tied back up to the post.

"About the time I was getting finished an old woman came out of the restaurant, hit me over the head with her cane, and started screamin' that I was stealin' her dog. I tried to explain that I was only tryin' to help, but she was too hysterical to listen, so I just got in the car and came home. She was standin' on the street wavin' her cane at me as I drove away. . . .

"Do you know, I don't think I ever want to go to the city again."

City
People

Not often, but sometimes, the stories in Bert's Cafe were about city people and how little they knew about country life. There were the usual stories about city hunters shooting cows and then strapping them to their cars thinking they had killed trophy moose or elk, and there were others too.

Sparky Anderson told about a group of city hunters who shot his Muscovy ducks right in his barnyard. "They shot them from their car," Sparky said, "and then came to the house to ask permission to go get them."

Charlie Maystead told about a city cousin of his who came to visit when he was a kid. "We had the wood cookstove then," Charlie said, "and one morning this cousin got up early and decided to put the coffee on. We all woke up a little while later with the house full of smoke. Come to find out he had built the fire in the oven."

Pete Hawkins told about a friend of his son in university who came to visit the farm. "He wondered who had mowed the grass in the pasture," Pete said.

Bert told a story one time about some city people traveling through town who stopped at his restaurant for lunch. "My special that day was beef tongue," Bert said. "One of them looked at me and said, 'Tongue! I ain't eating anything that comes out of a cow's mouth. Bring me some eggs.' "

There were lots of stories in Deer River about city people getting lost. Some of them were just variations of the old tale about the traveler who stops and asks a farmer directions. At first the farmer tells the traveler to follow the road west, then changes his mind and says to follow the road east, and finally informs the traveler that he can't get to where he's going from where he is now.

Another story depicts a farmer out for devilment who sends an enquiring traveler, through a series of complicated directions, on a circuitous route back to the point where he started. "You've sent me in a circle," the traveler said.

"Just wanted to see if you could follow directions," said the farmer.

"You're a fool," said the traveler.

"It ain't me that's lost," said the farmer.

One time a traveler stopped Tom Hannah while he was in town and asked him how to find the Hannah residence. Tom didn't recognize the man, but asked, "Do you know those people?" The stranger said that he did, so Tom told him to follow the main road out of town until he got to where the old schoolhouse used to be. Then he told him to turn west and follow that road until two miles before Hoppingarner Corners. Then he said he should go south until he came to where Pete Hawkins was baling alfalfa. "Turn left there unless Pete's baling brome grass," Tom said, "in which case you go up the road until you get to where they're talking about building the new United Church." Tom told the fellow that he could turn there and follow the road right to the house. "But look out," Tom warned the stranger, "Tom Hannah don't like strangers, you know."

The fellow thanked Tom just like he had been talking sensible and drove off. Tom said that he never did show up at his house, though.

Jake Peters told about the time he took a city friend hunting down in the sandhills south of Deer River. "We stopped and made a camp to have dinner," Jake said, "and I sent him down to the creek for some water. Pretty soon he came running back looking like he'd seen a ghost. 'There's a bear down in the creek,' he said.

"I told him he should have just gone ahead and got the water, that the bear was just as afraid of him as he was of it. He looked at me in disbelief and then said, 'Well, if that's the case, there was no need to get the water because it wouldn't be fit to drink anyway.'"

Epilogue: How to Tell a Story

If you want to be a good storyteller your first and most important rule should be to love the tale you plan to tell. If you don't feel something special about a story, leave it for someone to tell who does. All stories have a magic of their own, but you can't convey that magic unless you feel it yourself. Remember: Good storytelling is a creative process. When you tell a story you give the listener a part of yourself.

Before you tell your stories to others, practice telling them to yourself. Tell your practice stories over and over again while you're lying in bed, driving a car, or taking a walk. Listen to the sound of the words, and the way they sound together. Then, when you are satisfied with the tale you're telling to yourself, tell it to anyone you can find who'll listen. As every storyteller knows, the more you tell them, the better your stories will become. Sparky used to say that he had told some of his stories so often that he believed them himself.

Never memorize a story word for word from a book or recording. Instead, when you tell the story, think of the images the tale created in your mind when you first read or heard it, and then tell the story in your own way. Remember: You can't tell a story wrong. There are hundreds of ways to tell the same tale, and no single way is necessarily better than another.

When you learn a story from a book, read it over half a dozen times even before you tell it to yourself. Think about the images you see as you read the story. Listen for words and catch phrases that will help you through the story when you tell it—words like, "I'm going to huff and puff and blow your house in," in the story of the three little pigs, or my reference to the "clucker coop" in Pete's story about the hoop snake.

Think about the words you will say and the way they sound together. Decide what changes you will make to the story—if any—that will make it a better tale for you. When, as you read the story, you reach a point where you can clearly hear the tale you are going to tell, you are ready to begin practicing. First, read over the story a final time to make sure you have everything right; then begin telling the story to yourself. When you're comfortable telling the tale that way, start telling it to others.

Many stories, of course, you will learn from other storytellers. When you hear a story you like, make it your own. It's not really stealing. Stories have a life independent of any single teller, and every storyteller has a responsibility to help keep them alive. Besides, although you might not realize it now, even when you tell a story you have learned from someone else, you are changing its spirit, putting in something of yourself, making it your own.

Some stories you can create entirely yourself from events that happen to you or people you know. You should never limit your story to the details of any particular incident, though. If you want to tell good stories, expand on the facts. Dramatize the proceedings. As Sparky always said, "It's barely worth talking if you're going to tell the truth."

One more thing. If you should happen to blunder while telling a story, disguise the error as best you can and go on. Never admit to a mistake. If you suddenly realize that you have omitted an interesting, but unimportant, detail, forget it. Don't muddle your yarn trying to clear up previous mistakes.

If you've left out a necessary link in your tale, put it in as skillfully and unobtrusively as you can, and go on. Make it appear as if you are telling the story exactly as you intended to tell it.

Stopping to explain an error only increases the distraction your listener must surmount to appreciate your tale.

Always, when telling a story, you should be more concerned about the tale you want to tell than you are with yourself or your methods of storytelling. For the most part stories come through you, not from you. Stories have a life of their own, and while you give something of yourself, of your own personality, in the telling, your listener will bring a part of himself to the story too—and his contribution is equally as important.

If we're lucky, he'll take your story, as he interprets it, and pass it along to someone else. By the time you hear it again, you might not recognize it.

PHOTO BY ANNA WOODS

ABOUT THE AUTHOR

Ted Stone is a freelance writer—a weekly column for the *Winnipeg Free Press* and articles for publications throughout Canada and the United States as diverse as *Manitoba Business* and *Blair and Ketchum's Country Journal*.

He has been interested in storytelling all his life and has actively pursued that interest through radio, as well as oral and written expressions. He has appeared on Morningside to discuss the art and prepared a radio documentary about American Indian storytelling for school broadcasts. Across the continent, storytelling groups and festivals are springing up, trying to capture some of the magic of the dying art. *Hailstorms and Hoop Snakes* will add immeasurably to that revival.

Ted Stone lives with his family on a small farm near Ericsdale, Manitoba. His interest in agriculture finds practical expression in raising a variety of livestock, and he enjoys reading, music, bird watching, and above all collecting and telling stories.